HMH

math
expressions

Dr. Karen C. Fuson

Watch the platypus come alive in its watery world as you discover and solve math challenges.

Download the *Math Worlds AR* app available on Android or iOS devices.

Grade 2

Volume 2

NSF

This material is based upon work supported by the
National Science Foundation
under Grant Numbers
ESI-9816320, REC-9806020, and RED-935373.

Any opinions, findings, and conclusions, or recommendations expressed in this material
are those of the author and do not necessarily reflect the views of the National Science Foundation.

BIG IDEA 3 - Word Problems: Addition and Subtraction Within 100

Dear Family:

In this unit, your child will find the value of various coin combinations. Children will also combine different coins to equal one dollar.

25¢ + 25¢ + 10¢ + 10¢ + 10¢ + 10¢ + 10¢ = 100¢

Then your child will count both dollars and coins.

Say: $1.00 $1.25 $1.35 $1.40

You can help at home by providing opportunities for your child to practice counting money. Begin with amounts less than $1.00.

Please contact me if you have any questions or concerns. Thank you for helping your child to learn mathematics.

Sincerely,
Your child's teacher

Estimada familia:

En esta unidad su niño va a hallar el valor de diversas combinaciones de monedas. Los niños también combinarán diferentes monedas para igualar el valor de un dólar.

$$25¢ + 25¢ + 10¢ + 10¢ + 10¢ + 10¢ + 10¢ = 100¢$$

Luego, su niño contará billetes de dólares y monedas.

Se dice: $1.00 $1.25 $1.35 $1.40

Usted puede ayudar a su niño proporcionándole en casa oportunidades de practicar contando dinero. Empiece con cantidades menores que $1.00.

Si tiene alguna duda o algún comentario, por favor comuníquese conmigo. Gracias por ayudar a su niño a aprender matemáticas.

Atentamente,
El maestro de su niño

Explore Quarters

difference

estimate

round

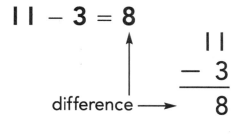

difference

Make a reasonable guess about how many or how much.

Express a number to the nearest ten or hundred. You can round down or round up.

52 —→ 50   278 —→ 300

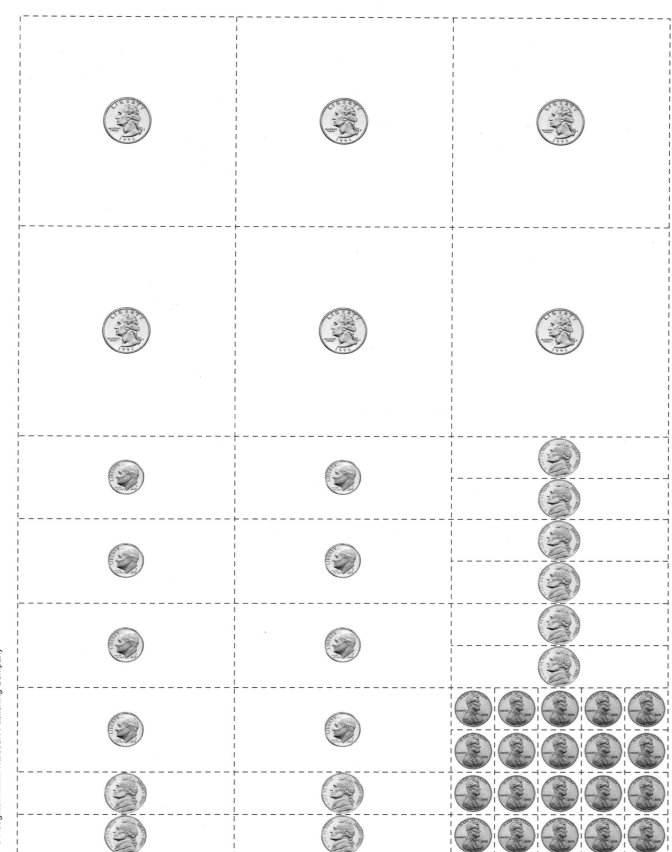

Cut on dashed lines.

© Houghton Mifflin Harcourt Publishing Company

Coin Cards

Cut on dashed lines.

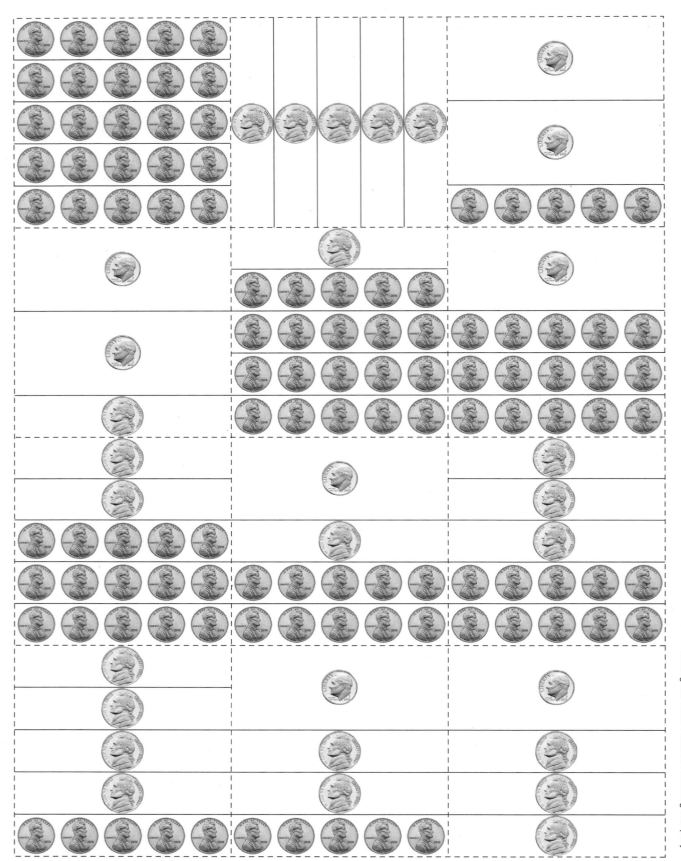

Cut only on dashed lines.

Quarter Squares (back)

Name _____

Make 25 Cents

Draw the correct coins to show 25¢.

1 pennies

_____

2 nickels

_____

3 dimes and nickels

_____

4 any coins

Find the Money Amount

Read the sentence. Draw the coins.
Find the total amount.

5 Louise has 2 quarters and 1 dime.

_____ ¢

6 Ned has 5 dimes and 3 nickels.

_____ ¢

7 Vic has 4 nickels and 5 pennies.

_____ ¢

8 Olga has 3 quarters and 9 pennies.

_____ ¢

✓ **Check Understanding**

Explain how to show 53 cents using only quarters and pennies.

Cut on dashed lines.

Dollar Equivalents (front) **205**

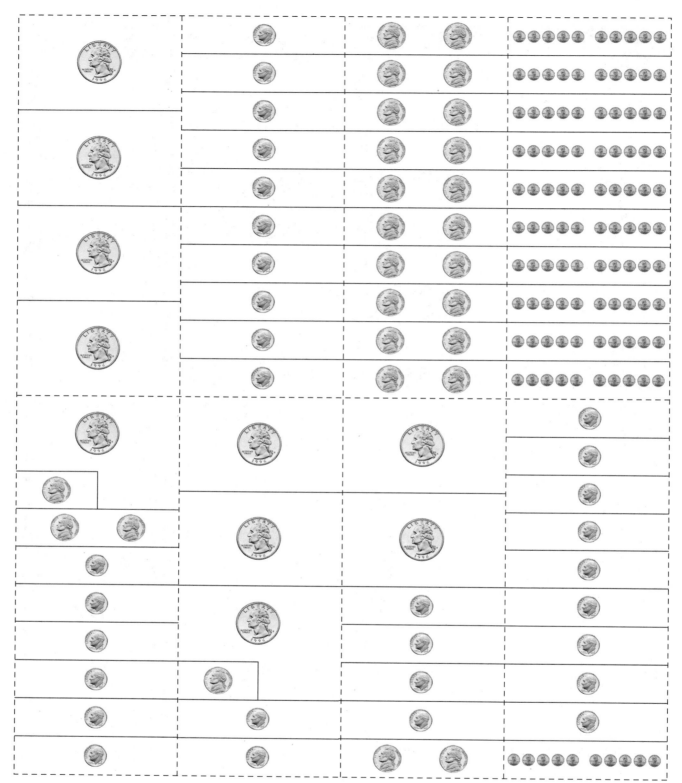

Cut only on dashed lines.

Dollar Equivalents (back)

Name _____

Count Coins and Bills

Under each picture, write the total amount of money so far.
Then write the total using $. The first exercise is done for you.

25¢	25¢	10¢	5¢

25¢	50¢	60¢	65¢

$ _0_ . _6_ _5_
total

---

②

25¢	10¢	10¢	1¢	1¢

| ___ | ___ | ___ | ___ | ___ |

$ ___ . ___ ___
total

---

③

100¢	25¢	5¢	5¢

| ___ | ___ | ___ | ___ |

$ ___ . ___ ___
total

---

④ Bo has 1 dollar, 2 quarters, 1 dime, 4 nickels, and 3 pennies.

Draw s, s, ⑩ s, ⑤ s, and ① s.

Write the total amount of money. $ ___ . ___ ___
total

Explore Dollars **207**

What's the Error?

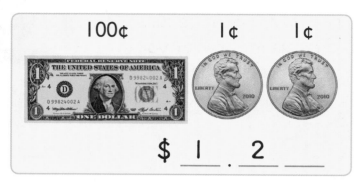 

100¢   1¢   1¢

$ __1__ . __2__

I wrote the total. Did I make a mistake?

5 Show Puzzled Penguin how you would find the total amount of money. Under each picture, write the total amount so far.

100¢   1¢   1¢

_____   _____   _____ $ ____.____ ____

total

More Practice Writing Totals

6   100¢   5¢   1¢   1¢

_____   _____   _____   _____ $ ____.____ ____

total

✓ Check Understanding

What is the value of 1 dollar bill, 2 quarters, 3 dimes, 2 nickels, and 1 penny?

_____

Explore Dollars

Name _____ Date _____

Under the picture, write the total amount so far. Use ¢.
Then write the total using $.

1 25¢   25¢   10¢   10¢   10¢   10¢   5¢   1¢

25¢   50¢   60¢   70¢   80¢   90¢   _____   _____

$ _____ . _____ _____
                    total

2   100¢   25¢   10¢   5¢   5¢

100¢   125¢   135¢   _____

$ _____ . _____ _____
                    total

3 Abbie has 1 dollar, 1 quarter, 1 dime, 2 nickels, and
3 pennies. Draw ⃞100 s, ⃝25 s, ⃝10 s, ⃝5 s, and ⃝1 s
to show her money.

Write the total amount of money. $ _____ . _____ _____
                                                          total

Name _____ Date _____

PATH to
FLUENCY

Add or subtract.

1 $4 + 3 = \boxed{}$ **2** $11 + 7 = \boxed{}$ **3** $9 + 5 = \boxed{}$

4 $12 - 6 = \boxed{}$ **5** $10 - 6 = \boxed{}$ **6** $17 - 9 = \boxed{}$

7
$$\begin{array}{r} 14 \\ -\ 12 \\ \hline \end{array}$$

8
$$\begin{array}{r} 14 \\ -\ \ 6 \\ \hline \end{array}$$

9
$$\begin{array}{r} 20 \\ -\ \ 9 \\ \hline \end{array}$$

10
$$\begin{array}{r} 40 \\ +\ 10 \\ \hline \end{array}$$

11
$$\begin{array}{r} 30 \\ +\ 38 \\ \hline \end{array}$$

12
$$\begin{array}{r} 53 \\ +\ 17 \\ \hline \end{array}$$

13
$$\begin{array}{r} 54 \\ +\ 38 \\ \hline \end{array}$$

14
$$\begin{array}{r} 71 \\ +\ 13 \\ \hline \end{array}$$

15
$$\begin{array}{r} 62 \\ +\ 38 \\ \hline \end{array}$$

Name _____

Word Problems: Ungrouping 100

When you subtract, you can use the following drawings to help you ungroup.

Use Dollars to Ungroup

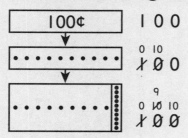

Use Quick Tens to Ungroup

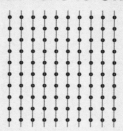

Solve the word problems.

Show your work.

1 The baker bakes 100 loaves of bread. He sells 73 loaves. How many loaves are left?

☐ _____
label

2 Jim has 100 flowers in his garden. He gives 35 of them away. How many flowers are left in Jim's garden?

☐ _____
label

3 The letter carrier has 100 letters in her bag. She delivers 52 letters. How many letters are left in her bag?

☐ _____
label

© Houghton Mifflin Harcourt Publishing Company

Subtract from 100

Solve. Rewrite the hundred or make a drawing.

④ $100 - 62 = \boxed{}$

⑤ $100 - 83 = \boxed{}$

⑥ $100 - 79 = \boxed{}$

⑦ $100 - 54 = \boxed{}$

✓ Check Understanding

Explain how to find the solution for $100 = 37 + \square$.

Addends and Subtraction

Name _____

Write and Solve Word Problems

Write a word problem to match the equation.

Use any method to solve the problem.

Show your work.

---

1 $63 - 35 =$ ☐

_____

_____

_____

_____

_____

---

2 $92 - 54 =$ ☐

_____

_____

_____

_____

_____

Use Various Methods to Solve Problems

3 Read the problem. Write the equation in vertical form. Solve using the Expanded Method.

Barb and Yohan picked 41 daisies. Barb picked 23 daisies. How many daisies did Yohan pick?

$$\begin{array}{r} - \\ \hline \end{array}$$

_____ daisies

4 Read the problem. Write the equation in vertical form. Solve using the Ungroup First Method.

There are 82 yellow blocks in the bin. There are 57 pink blocks in the bin. How many more yellow blocks than pink blocks are in the bin?

$$\begin{array}{r} - \\ \hline \end{array}$$

_____ more yellow blocks

Use any method to solve. Show your work.

5
$$\begin{array}{r} 7\,4 \\ -\,4\,8 \\ \hline \end{array}$$

6
$$\begin{array}{r} 5\,0 \\ -\,3\,7 \\ \hline \end{array}$$

 Check Understanding

Write one subtraction exercise that requires ungrouping a ten and one that does not.

Subtraction Word Problems

Dear Family:

In this program, children learn these two methods for 2-digit subtraction. However, children may use any method that they understand, can explain, and can do fairly quickly.

Expanded Method	Ungroup First Method
Step 1 "Expand" each number to show that it is made up of tens and ones. $$64 = 60 + 4$$ $$-28 = 20 + 8$$ **Step 2** Check to see if there are enough ones to subtract from. If not, ungroup a ten into 10 ones and add it to the existing ones. $$64 = \overset{50}{\cancel{60}} + \overset{14}{\cancel{4}}$$ $$-28 = 20 + 8$$ **Step 3** Subtract to find the answer. Children may subtract from left to right or from right to left. $$64 = \overset{50}{\cancel{60}} + \overset{14}{\cancel{4}}$$ $$-28 = 20 + 8$$ $$\quad\quad 30 + 6 = 36$$	**Step 1** Check to see if there are enough ones to subtract from. If not, ungroup by opening up one of the 6 tens in 64 to be 10 ones. 4 ones plus these new 10 ones make 14 ones. We draw a magnifying glass around the top number to help children focus on the regrouping.  **Step 2** Subtract to find the answer. Children may subtract from left to right or from right to left. 

In explaining any method they use, children are expected to use "tens and ones" language. This shows that they understand they are subtracting 2 tens from 5 tens (not 2 from 5) and 8 ones from 14 ones.

Please contact me if you have any questions or comments.

Sincerely,
Your child's teacher

Estimada familia:

En este programa, los niños aprenden estos dos métodos para restar con números de 2 dígitos. Sin embargo, pueden usar cualquier método que comprendan, puedan explicar y puedan hacer relativamente rápido.

Método extendido	Método de desagrupar primero
Paso 1 "Extender" cada número para mostrar que consta de decenas y unidades. $$64 = 60 + 4$$ $$- 28 = 20 + 8$$ **Paso 2** Observar si hay suficientes unidades para restar. Si no las hay, desagrupar una decena para formar 10 unidades y sumarla a las unidades existentes. $$64 = \overset{50}{\cancel{60}} + \overset{14}{\cancel{4}}$$ $$- 28 = 20 + 8$$ **Paso 3** Restar para hallar la respuesta. Los niños pueden restar de izquierda a derecha o de derecha a izquierda. $$64 = \overset{50}{\cancel{60}} + \overset{14}{\cancel{4}}$$ $$- 28 = 20 + 8$$ $$30 + 6 = 36$$	**Paso 1** Observar si hay suficientes unidades para restar. Si no las hay, desagrupar una de las 6 decenas en 64 para obtener 10 unidades. 4 unidades más las 10 unidades nuevas son 14 unidades. Dibujamos una lupa alrededor del número superior para ayudar a los niños a concentrarse en desagrupar. 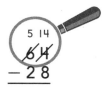 **Paso 2** Restar para hallar la respuesta. Los niños pueden restar de izquierda a derecha o de derecha a izquierda. 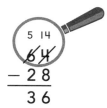

Cuando los niños expliquen el método que usan, deben hacerlo usando un lenguaje relacionado con "decenas y unidades". Esto demuestra que comprenden que están restando 2 decenas de 5 decenas (no 2 de 5) y 8 unidades de 14 unidades.

Si tiene alguna duda o algún comentario, por favor comuníquese conmigo.

Atentamente,
El maestro de su niño

Explain the Expanded Method

Mr. Green likes this method. Explain what he does.

Step 1	Step 2	Step 3
$64 = 60 + 4$	$64 = \overset{50}{\cancel{60}} + \overset{14}{\cancel{4}}$	$64 = \overset{50}{\cancel{60}} + \overset{14}{\cancel{4}}$
$- 28 = 20 + 8$	$- 28 = 20 + 8$	$- 28 = 20 + 8$
		$30 + 6 = 36$

Try the Expanded Method

Show your work numerically and with a proof drawing.

1
$$
\begin{array}{r}
42 \\
- 19 \\
\hline
\end{array}
$$

2
$$
\begin{array}{r}
75 \\
- 46 \\
\hline
\end{array}
$$

3
$$
\begin{array}{r}
81 \\
- 37 \\
\hline
\end{array}
$$

Explain the Ungroup First Method

Mrs. Green likes this method. Explain what she does.

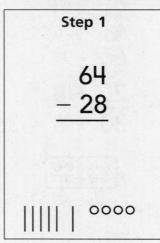

Step 1

$$64$$
$$- 28$$

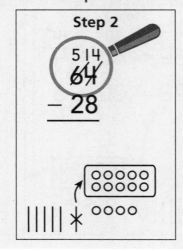

Step 2

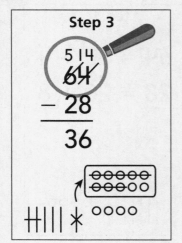

Step 3

Try the Ungroup First Method

Show your work numerically and with a proof drawing.

4

$$42$$
$$- 19$$

_____

5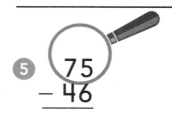

$$75$$
$$- 46$$

_____

6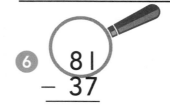

$$81$$
$$- 37$$

✓ **Check Understanding**

Describe two different ways to solve $46 - 17 = \square$.

Two Methods of Subtraction

Name _____

VOCABULARY
difference

Solve and Discuss

Subtract to find the **difference**.

1.
$$
\begin{array}{r}
75 \\
-47 \\
\hline
\end{array}
$$

2.
$$
\begin{array}{r}
54 \\
-18 \\
\hline
\end{array}
$$

3.
$$
\begin{array}{r}
94 \\
-36 \\
\hline
\end{array}
$$

4.
$$
\begin{array}{r}
66 \\
-34 \\
\hline
\end{array}
$$

5.
$$
\begin{array}{r}
85 \\
-58 \\
\hline
\end{array}
$$

6.
$$
\begin{array}{r}
89 \\
-69 \\
\hline
\end{array}
$$

7.
$$
\begin{array}{r}
82 \\
-59 \\
\hline
\end{array}
$$

8.
$$
\begin{array}{r}
97 \\
-78 \\
\hline
\end{array}
$$

9.
$$
\begin{array}{r}
65 \\
-28 \\
\hline
\end{array}
$$

10.
$$
\begin{array}{r}
78 \\
-19 \\
\hline
\end{array}
$$

11.
$$
\begin{array}{r}
53 \\
-26 \\
\hline
\end{array}
$$

12.
$$
\begin{array}{r}
91 \\
-46 \\
\hline
\end{array}
$$

What's the Error?

$$\begin{array}{r} 13 \\ 8\!\!\!/ \\[-2pt] -5\,5 \\ \hline 3\,8 \end{array}$$

Did I make a mistake?

13 Show Puzzled Penguin how you would subtract.
Make a proof drawing to check your work.

$$\begin{array}{r} 8\,3 \\ -5\,5 \\ \hline \end{array}$$

PATH to FLUENCY Add and Subtract Within 20

Add or subtract.

14 $9 + 4 = \boxed{}$ **15** $6 + 5 = \boxed{}$ **16** $3 + 4 = \boxed{}$

17 $\begin{array}{r} 8 \\ +\ 7 \\ \hline \end{array}$ **18** $\begin{array}{r} 4 \\ +\ 8 \\ \hline \end{array}$ **19** $\begin{array}{r} 5 \\ +\ 9 \\ \hline \end{array}$

20 $17 - 8 = \boxed{}$ **21** $13 - 5 = \boxed{}$ **22** $14 - 7 = \boxed{}$

23 $\begin{array}{r} 9 \\ -\ 6 \\ \hline \end{array}$ **24** $\begin{array}{r} 1\,5 \\ -\ 6 \\ \hline \end{array}$ **25** $\begin{array}{r} 1\,6 \\ -\ 8 \\ \hline \end{array}$

 Check Understanding
Make a proof drawing to solve $65 - 27 = \square$.

Practice and Explain a Method

Explain Ungrouping 200

Use this drawing to explain why 200 = 100 + 90 + 10.

Review Both Methods

Expanded Method

$$
\begin{array}{ccccccc}
& & & 100 & \overset{90}{\cancel{100}} & \overset{10}{\cancel{0}} & \\
200 & = & 200 & + \cancel{0} & + \cancel{0} & \text{or} & 200 + \overset{90}{\cancel{0}} + \overset{10}{\cancel{0}} \\
- 68 & = & & 60 & + 8 & & \\
\hline
& & 100 & + 30 & + 2 & = 132 &
\end{array}
$$

100 + 30 + 2 = 132

Ungroup First Method

Ungroup in two steps.   or   **Ungroup all at once.**

Step 1.   Ungroup
I hundred to
make 10 tens.

Step 2.   Ungroup 1 ten
to make 10 ones.

$$
\begin{array}{r}
\overset{9}{1}\cancel{1}0\,10 \\
200 \\
- \quad 68 \\
\hline
132
\end{array}
$$
or
$$
\begin{array}{r}
1\ 9\ 10 \\
200 \\
- \quad 68 \\
\hline
132
\end{array}
$$

Ungroup
I hundred
to make
9 tens and
10 ones.

200 = 100 + 90 + 10

Explain how ungrouping and subtraction work.
Relate the steps used in these methods to the drawing
at the top of the page.

Practice the Ungroup First Method

Use the Ungroup First Method to find each difference.

1. $$\begin{array}{r} 2\ 0\ 0 \\ -\ \ 8\ 7 \\ \hline \end{array}$$

2. $$\begin{array}{r} 2\ 0\ 0 \\ -\ \ 8\ 9 \\ \hline \end{array}$$

3. $$\begin{array}{r} 2\ 0\ 0 \\ -\ \ 4\ 6 \\ \hline \end{array}$$

4. $$\begin{array}{r} 2\ 0\ 0 \\ -\ \ 3\ 8 \\ \hline \end{array}$$

5. $$\begin{array}{r} 2\ 0\ 0 \\ -\ \ 2\ 7 \\ \hline \end{array}$$

6. $$\begin{array}{r} 2\ 0\ 0 \\ -\ \ 8\ 2 \\ \hline \end{array}$$

✓ **Check Understanding**

Talk with a partner about ungrouping 200.
How is using the Expanded Method different
from using the Ungroup First Method?
How is it the same?

Subtract from 200

Name _____

Decide When to Ungroup

Decide if you need to ungroup. Then subtract.

1
```
  1 6 3
-   8 9
```

Did you ungroup a ten to get more ones? _____
Did you ungroup a hundred to get more tens? _____

2
```
  1 3 4
-   7 3
```

Did you ungroup a ten to get more ones? _____
Did you ungroup a hundred to get more tens? _____

3
```
  1 5 8
-   3 7
```

Did you ungroup a ten to get more ones? _____
Did you ungroup a hundred to get more tens? _____

4
```
  1 3 8
-   5 9
```

Did you ungroup a ten to get more ones? _____
Did you ungroup a hundred to get more tens? _____

5
```
  1 4 6
-   5 7
```

Did you ungroup a ten to get more ones? _____
Did you ungroup a hundred to get more tens? _____

6
```
  1 4 6
-   3 5
```

Did you ungroup a ten to get more ones? _____
Did you ungroup a hundred to get more tens? _____

Decide When to Ungroup (continued)

Decide if you need to ungroup. Then subtract.

7
```
  1 6 7
-   4 2
```

Did you ungroup a ten to get more ones? _____
Did you ungroup a hundred to get more tens? _____

8
```
  1 4 8
-   3 9
```

Did you ungroup a ten to get more ones? _____
Did you ungroup a hundred to get more tens? _____

9
```
  1 2 4
-   8 6
```

Did you ungroup a ten to get more ones? _____
Did you ungroup a hundred to get more tens? _____

10
```
  1 5 0
-   2 7
```

Did you ungroup a ten to get more ones? _____
Did you ungroup a hundred to get more tens? _____

✔ Check Understanding

Circle the correct answer to complete each sentence.

If there are enough tens to subtract from,
I _____ need to ungroup.   do / do not

If there are not enough ones to subtract from,
I _____ need to ungroup.   do / do not

Ungroup from the Left or from the Right

Name _____

Subtract with Zeros

Decide if you need to ungroup. Then subtract.

1.
$$
\begin{array}{r}
1\ 0\ 8 \\
-\quad 4\ 6 \\
\hline
\end{array}
$$

2.
$$
\begin{array}{r}
1\ 0\ 3 \\
-\quad 6\ 5 \\
\hline
\end{array}
$$

3.
$$
\begin{array}{r}
1\ 5\ 0 \\
-\quad 7\ 9 \\
\hline
\end{array}
$$

4.
$$
\begin{array}{r}
1\ 0\ 2 \\
-\quad 8\ 3 \\
\hline
\end{array}
$$

5.
$$
\begin{array}{r}
1\ 6\ 0 \\
-\quad 9\ 2 \\
\hline
\end{array}
$$

6.
$$
\begin{array}{r}
1\ 0\ 7 \\
-\quad 6\ 1 \\
\hline
\end{array}
$$

7.
$$
\begin{array}{r}
1\ 0\ 6 \\
-\quad 3\ 8 \\
\hline
\end{array}
$$

8.
$$
\begin{array}{r}
1\ 7\ 0 \\
-\quad 4\ 0 \\
\hline
\end{array}
$$

9.
$$
\begin{array}{r}
1\ 8\ 0 \\
-\quad 9\ 3 \\
\hline
\end{array}
$$

10.
$$
\begin{array}{r}
1\ 4\ 0 \\
-\quad 5\ 7 \\
\hline
\end{array}
$$

11.
$$
\begin{array}{r}
1\ 5\ 0 \\
-\quad 5\ 4 \\
\hline
\end{array}
$$

12.
$$
\begin{array}{r}
1\ 0\ 6 \\
-\quad 4\ 3 \\
\hline
\end{array}
$$

Zero in the Ones or Tens Place **225**

Solve and Discuss

Decide if you need to ungroup. Then subtract.

⑬ $\begin{array}{r} 106 \\ -81 \\ \hline \end{array}$　　⑭ $\begin{array}{r} 110 \\ -18 \\ \hline \end{array}$　　⑮ $\begin{array}{r} 190 \\ -72 \\ \hline \end{array}$

⑯ $\begin{array}{r} 107 \\ -38 \\ \hline \end{array}$　　⑰ $\begin{array}{r} 130 \\ -22 \\ \hline \end{array}$　　⑱ $\begin{array}{r} 120 \\ -63 \\ \hline \end{array}$

Solve the word problem. Make a
math drawing if you need more help.

Show your work.

⑲ Mrs. Dash grilled 110 burgers for the
school picnic. 79 were eaten. How many
burgers are left?

label

✓ Check Understanding

Write the subtraction 120 − 63. Subtract by
ungrouping from the left. Then solve the same
problem by ungrouping from the right.

　　　Zero in the Ones or Tens Place

Name _____

Act It Out

First, see how much money you have. Then decide what to buy. Pay for the item. Then write how much money you have left.

Yard Sale

Cork Board   Toy Rabbit   Toy Guitar   Perfume   Knit Cap
78¢   84¢   75¢   89¢   99¢

1 I have 162¢ in my pocket.

I buy the _____.

```
  1 6 2 ¢
- ┌──────┐
  │      │ ¢
  └──────┘
```

I have _____ ¢ left.

2 I have 143¢ in my pocket.

I buy the _____.

```
  1 4 3 ¢
- ┌──────┐
  │      │ ¢
  └──────┘
```

I have _____ ¢ left.

3 I have 154¢ in my pocket.

I buy the _____.

```
  1 5 4 ¢
- ┌──────┐
  │      │ ¢
  └──────┘
```

I have _____ ¢ left.

4 I have 126¢ in my pocket.

I buy the _____.

```
  1 2 6 ¢
- ┌──────┐
  │      │ ¢
  └──────┘
```

I have _____ ¢ left.

Model Subtraction with Money **227**

Use a Dollar Sign

Write the money amount. The first one is done for you.

5 134¢ = __1__ dollar __3__ dimes __4__ pennies = $ __1__ . __3__ __4__

6 76¢ = ___ dollars ___ dimes ___ pennies = $ ___ . ___ ___

7 179¢ = ___ dollar ___ dimes ___ pennies = $ ___ . ___ ___

8 58¢ = ___ dollars ___ dimes ___ pennies = $ ___ . ___ ___

Find the difference. Use play money to help you ungroup, if you wish.

9	**10**	**11**
$ 1 . 4 4 − . 2 3	$ 1 . 2 5 − . 9 5	$ 1 . 6 3 − . 9 5
12	**13**	**14**
$ 1 . 5 8 − . 4 5	$ 1 . 3 6 − . 7 5	$ 1 . 9 2 − . 9 5

 Check Understanding

Explain how to ungroup $1.56 to pay for an item that costs 88¢.

Model Subtraction with Money

Name _____

(PATH to FLUENCY) Subtract Within 100

Subtract.

1. $\begin{array}{r} 65 \\ -16 \\ \hline \end{array}$

2. $\begin{array}{r} 58 \\ -37 \\ \hline \end{array}$

3. $\begin{array}{r} 20 \\ -14 \\ \hline \end{array}$

4. $\begin{array}{r} 74 \\ -23 \\ \hline \end{array}$

5. $\begin{array}{r} 19 \\ -17 \\ \hline \end{array}$

6. $\begin{array}{r} 50 \\ -13 \\ \hline \end{array}$

7. $\begin{array}{r} 87 \\ -30 \\ \hline \end{array}$

8. $\begin{array}{r} 91 \\ -45 \\ \hline \end{array}$

9. $\begin{array}{r} 31 \\ -\ 9 \\ \hline \end{array}$

10. $\begin{array}{r} 97 \\ -79 \\ \hline \end{array}$

11. $\begin{array}{r} 20 \\ -\ 7 \\ \hline \end{array}$

12. $\begin{array}{r} 46 \\ -36 \\ \hline \end{array}$

(PATH to FLUENCY) **Subtract Within 100** (continued)

Subtract.

⑬
$$\begin{array}{r} 100 \\ -\ 48 \\ \hline \end{array}$$

⑭
$$\begin{array}{r} 67 \\ -31 \\ \hline \end{array}$$

⑮
$$\begin{array}{r} 55 \\ -16 \\ \hline \end{array}$$

⑯
$$\begin{array}{r} 83 \\ -\ 8 \\ \hline \end{array}$$

⑰
$$\begin{array}{r} 40 \\ -26 \\ \hline \end{array}$$

⑱
$$\begin{array}{r} 19 \\ -11 \\ \hline \end{array}$$

⑲
$$\begin{array}{r} 14 \\ -11 \\ \hline \end{array}$$

⑳
$$\begin{array}{r} 25 \\ -12 \\ \hline \end{array}$$

㉑
$$\begin{array}{r} 100 \\ -\ 19 \\ \hline \end{array}$$

㉒
$$\begin{array}{r} 94 \\ -76 \\ \hline \end{array}$$

㉓
$$\begin{array}{r} 20 \\ -\ 8 \\ \hline \end{array}$$

㉔
$$\begin{array}{r} 77 \\ -24 \\ \hline \end{array}$$

✓ **Check Understanding**

Circle the correct answer to complete each sentence.

When subtracting 78 − 25, I _____ ungroup.   do / do not

When subtracting 78 − 29, I _____ ungroup.   do / do not

Fluency: Subtraction Within 100

Name _____

PATH to FLUENCY *Ungroup Challenge*

Work in 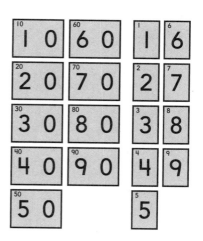. Lay out Secret Code Cards like this.

| 10 | 60 | 1 | 6 |
| 1 0 | 6 0 | 1 | 6 |

2 0 | 7 0 | 2 | 7

3 0 | 8 0 | 3 | 8

4 0 | 9 0 | 4 | 9

5 0 | | 5

1 Use Secret Code Cards to help you make a 2-digit subtraction (the top number must be less than 100).

| 60 | | 2 |
| 6 0 | | 2 |

| 30 | | 7 |
| 3 0 | | 7 |

$$\begin{array}{r} {}^{5\ 12} \\ \cancel{6}\cancel{2} \\ -37 \\ \hline 25 \end{array}$$

2 Make another 2-digit subtraction.
- Use the same tens cards.
- If  *ungrouped a ten,* use ones cards that *do not need more ones.*

- If  *did not ungroup a ten,* use ones cards that *need more ones.*

| 60 | | 4 |
| 6 0 | | 4 |

| 30 | | 1 |
| 3 0 | | 1 |

$$\begin{array}{r} 64 \\ -31 \\ \hline 33 \end{array}$$

Activity continues on next page.

© Houghton Mifflin Harcourt Publishing Company

PATH to FLUENCY *Ungroup Challenge* (continued)

2 👥 Work together to check your work. Correct any errors.

3 Put the Secret Code Cards back. Switch roles and repeat. Continue until time is up.

To play the *Ungroup Challenge* as a game and compete with another pair, use the **Scoring Rules** below.

Scoring Rules for *Ungroup Challenge*

- Each player: Make two 2-digit subtractions (following the instructions from Step 1 on page 231). Do not check your work.

- Trade papers with another pair.

- Put a ✓ next to each correct answer. Put an **X** next to each incorrect answer.

- Give 1 point for each ✓. Subtract 3 points for each **X**.

- The pair with more points wins.

Fluency: Subtraction Within 100

Name _____

Date _____

Solve.   **Show your work.**

① $\begin{array}{r} 92 \\ -\ 47 \\ \hline \end{array}$

② $\begin{array}{r} 143 \\ -\ 81 \\ \hline \end{array}$

③ $\begin{array}{r} 126 \\ -\ 78 \\ \hline \end{array}$

④ $\begin{array}{r} 200 \\ -\ 79 \\ \hline \end{array}$

⑤ Kimberly has 164¢ in her pocket.
She buys a can of juice for 75¢.
How much money does she have left?

_____ ¢

Name _____ Date _____

PATH to
FLUENCY

Add or subtract.

1 $8 - 7 = \boxed{}$ **2** $13 - 5 = \boxed{}$ **3** $9 - 3 = \boxed{}$

4 $5 + 4 = \boxed{}$ **5** $7 + 5 = \boxed{}$ **6** $8 + 8 = \boxed{}$

7
$$\begin{array}{r} 47 \\ -\ 15 \\ \hline \end{array}$$

8
$$\begin{array}{r} 83 \\ -\ 14 \\ \hline \end{array}$$

9
$$\begin{array}{r} 56 \\ -\ 42 \\ \hline \end{array}$$

10
$$\begin{array}{r} 66 \\ +\ 20 \\ \hline \end{array}$$

11
$$\begin{array}{r} 31 \\ +\ 14 \\ \hline \end{array}$$

12
$$\begin{array}{r} 46 \\ +\ 29 \\ \hline \end{array}$$

13
$$\begin{array}{r} 88 \\ -\ 59 \\ \hline \end{array}$$

14
$$\begin{array}{r} 91 \\ -\ 67 \\ \hline \end{array}$$

15
$$\begin{array}{r} 100 \\ -\ 36 \\ \hline \end{array}$$

Addition and Subtraction Word Problems

Draw a Math Mountain to solve each word
problem. Write an equation to match.

① Teresa has 45 blocks. Then she
finds 29 more blocks under the
couch. How many blocks does
Teresa have now?

☐ _____
label

② The second grade art students make
163 masks. The art teacher displays
96 of the masks. How many masks are
not displayed?

☐ _____
label

③ There are 12 girls and 8 boys in
the library. How many children are
in the library altogether?

☐ _____
label

④ There are 90 glue sticks in the school
store. Then 52 glue sticks are sold.
How many glue sticks are left?

☐ _____
label

Addition and Subtraction Word Problems (continued)

Draw a Math Mountain to solve each word problem. Write an equation to match.

---

5 Sam has 47 baseball cards. Hank has 53 baseball cards. How many baseball cards do they have in all?

☐ _____
        label

---

6 Mrs. Snap has 42 pencils. She gives 29 pencils to her students and puts the rest in a box. How many pencils does she put in the box?

☐ _____
        label

---

7 At the park, Gabi collects 25 leaves. She collects 18 oak leaves, and the rest are maple leaves. How many are maple leaves?

☐ _____
        label

✓ **Check Understanding**

Explain how drawing a Math Mountain can help you decide whether to add or subtract to solve a word problem.

Word Problems with Addition and Subtraction

Find Equations for Math Mountains

1 Write all of the equations for 83, 59, and 24.

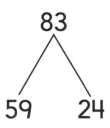

83

59   24

$59 + 24 = 83$ _____

_____

_____

$83 = 59 + 24$ _____

_____

_____

2 Write all of the equations for 142, 96, and 46.

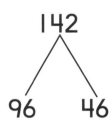

142

96   46

$96 + 46 = 142$ _____

_____

_____

$142 = 96 + 46$ _____

_____

_____

Word Problem Practice: Addition and Subtraction Within 20

Make a drawing. Write an equation. Solve.

---

3 There are 7 children at the lunch table.
Some more children sit down.
Then there are 11 children at the table.
How many children sit down?

☐ _____
label

---

4 Some leaves are on the ground. The children
pick up 9 leaves. Then there are 3 leaves on
the ground. How many leaves were on the
ground at the start?

☐ _____
label

---

5 Stevie has 8 more stickers than Ari.
Stevie has 13 stickers. How many
stickers does Ari have?

☐ _____
label

✓ Check Understanding

Draw and complete a Math Mountain with 100 at the
top and 45 on the bottom.

Equations with Greater Numbers

Name _____

PATH to FLUENCY Practice Addition and Subtraction Within 100

Add or subtract. Watch the sign!

1
```
  9 1
- 6 3
```

2
```
  3 6
+   9
```

3
```
  1 0 0
-   7 4
```

4
```
  4 5
+ 3 9
```

5
```
  6 4
- 2 3
```

6
```
  3 3
+ 6 6
```

7
```
  2 0
-   4
```

8
```
  3 4
+ 3 8
```

9
```
  5 2
- 3 8
```

10
```
  4 3
+ 5 7
```

11
```
  9 6
- 7 8
```

12
```
  1 3
+ 7 9
```

Solve and Discuss

Solve each word problem.   **Show your work.**

---

13 Mr. Hepburn bakes 48 muffins on Monday. On Tuesday, he bakes 24 muffins. How many muffins does he bake during those two days?

[   ] _____
              label

---

14 Mrs. Jennings gets 75 new books for the class library. She places 37 of them on the shelf. How many new books are left to place on the shelf?

[   ] _____
              label

---

15 Usain has 64 toy cars. He puts 25 of the cars into a box. How many cars are not in the box?

[   ] _____
              label

---

16 In June, Simone reads 18 books. In July, she reads 35 books. How many books does she read in June and July?

[   ] _____
              label

Practice Addition and Subtraction

Name _____

Round to the Nearest Ten

VOCABULARY
round

Round 32 to the nearest ten. Follow these steps:

Step 1: Underline the number in the tens place. **32**

Step 2: Write the ten that is greater than 32 above, and write the ten that is less than 32 below.

Step 3: Make a drawing to show each number.

Step 4: If there are 5 or more ones, round up. If there are fewer than 5 ones, round down.

40 ||||

32 |||∘∘   2 is less than 5, so round down.

30 |||

Practice Rounding

Round the number to the nearest ten.

You may use drawings.

17 13 ☐   **18** 18 ☐

19 22 ☐   **20** 44 ☐

21 36 ☐   **22** 55 ☐

Round to Estimate Answers

VOCABULARY
estimate

Round each number to the nearest ten.

Then add or subtract the rounded numbers.

Circle the answer that is the better **estimate**.

23
$$\begin{array}{r} 2\,1 \\ +\,1\,8 \\ \hline \end{array}$$

20 or 40

24
$$\begin{array}{r} 4\,2 \\ +\,2\,3 \\ \hline \end{array}$$

60 or 80

25
$$\begin{array}{r} 6\,7 \\ +\,1\,2 \\ \hline \end{array}$$

70 or 80

26
$$\begin{array}{r} 4\,4 \\ -\,2\,2 \\ \hline \end{array}$$

10 or 20

27
$$\begin{array}{r} 3\,8 \\ -\,1\,7 \\ \hline \end{array}$$

20 or 30

28
$$\begin{array}{r} 5\,1 \\ -\,3\,8 \\ \hline \end{array}$$

10 or 30

Solve by rounding.

Show your work.

29 At the picnic, 39 children chose apples and 12 chose oranges. Round each number to the nearest 10. *About* how many more children chose apples than oranges?

about ☐ _____
           label

✓ **Check Understanding**

Explain how you can use rounding to estimate $53 + 19$.

Practice Addition and Subtraction

Introduce the Juice Bar

Grapefruit Juice 11¢	Red Apple Juice 41¢	Lemon Juice 20¢	Pear Juice 22¢
Green Apple Juice 25¢	Peach Juice 40¢	Orange Juice 18¢	Cantaloupe Juice 10¢
Pineapple Juice 47¢	Raspberry Juice 33¢	Banana Juice 39¢	Watermelon Juice 15¢
Grape Juice 50¢	Celery Juice 36¢	Tomato Juice 30¢	Carrot Juice 29¢

Continue Buying and Selling

Choose two juice samples from the Juice Bar you would like to mix together. Find the total cost. Then find the change from one dollar.

1 I pick _____

and _____.

Juice 1 price: _____ ¢

Juice 2 price: + _____ ¢

Total: _____

100¢ − _____ = _____

My change is _____ ¢.

2 I pick _____

and _____.

Juice 1 price: _____ ¢

Juice 2 price: + _____ ¢

Total: _____

100¢ − _____ = _____

My change is _____ ¢.

3 I pick _____

and _____.

Juice 1 price: _____ ¢

Juice 2 price: + _____ ¢

Total: _____

100¢ − _____ = _____

My change is _____ ¢.

4 I pick _____

and _____.

Juice 1 price: _____ ¢

Juice 2 price: + _____ ¢

Total: _____

100¢ − _____ = _____

My change is _____ ¢.

✓ **Check Understanding**
Explain how to use the Adding Up Method to subtract 68¢ from $1.00.

Buy and Sell with One Dollar

Name _____

Practice the Adding Up Method

Add up to solve each word problem.   **Show your work.**

1 Tina has 62 baseball cards. After she goes shopping today, she will have 86 baseball cards. How many baseball cards is Tina going to buy?

☐ _____
        label

2 Myra has 87 dollars. She buys some gifts. Then she has 68 dollars. How much money does Myra spend on gifts?

☐ _____
        label

3 There are 15 apples in a basket. Some more apples are put in. Now there are 23 apples in the basket. How many apples are put in?

☐ _____
        label

4 Ms. Baylon put 113 pebbles in the fish tank. Some of the pebbles are brown. 54 of the pebbles are black. How many pebbles are brown?

☐ _____
        label

Practice the Adding Up Method (continued)

Add up to solve each word problem.   **Show your work.**

5 There are 25 bikes at a store. Then some more bikes are brought to the store. Now there are 48 bikes at the store. How many bikes are brought to the store?

☐ _____
          label

6 There are 95 pieces of popcorn in a bag. Sidney eats some of the pieces. Now there are 52 pieces in the bag. How many pieces does Sidney eat?

☐ _____
          label

7 In a package of stickers, there are 45 red stickers and some blue stickers. There are 100 stickers in all. How many stickers are blue?

☐ _____
          label

✓ **Check Understanding**

Choose a problem on this page. Make a drawing to show how you used the Adding Up Method to solve the problem.

Word Problems with Unknown Addends

Name _____

Practice the Adding Up Method

Add up to solve each word problem.   **Show your work.**

1 Last week, Justin read 27 comic books.
Erika read some comic books too. In all,
they read 86 comic books. How many
comic books did Erika read?

☐ _____
          label

2 In art class, the second grade boys and girls
drew 73 pictures. The girls drew 38 of the
pictures. How many pictures did the boys draw?

☐ _____
          label

3 There are 82 birds in the zoo. The zoo gets
some more birds. Now they have 100 birds.
How many birds does the zoo get?

☐ _____
          label

4 Mrs. Clark has 94 pens. She gives some
pens to her friends. Now she has 75 pens.
How many pens does Mrs. Clark give away?

☐ _____
          label

Practice the Adding Up Method (continued)

Add up to solve each word problem.   **Show your work.**

5 Ike has 54 crayons. His sister gives him
some more crayons. Now he has 82 crayons.
How many crayons does his sister give him?

[   ] _____
                label

6 In Mei's classroom, there are 39 books on a red shelf.
There are some books on a green shelf. There are
78 books on the two shelves. How many books are on
the green shelf?

[   ] _____
                label

PATH to FLUENCY Add and Subtract Within 100

Add or subtract.

7   2 2   **8**   1 7   **9**   5 1   **10**   8 6
      + 3 0   +   3   + 3 4   +   9

11 1 0 0   **12**   9 2   **13**   8 3   **14**   5 4
      −   6 8   − 1 5   − 7 7   − 2 9

✓ **Check Understanding**
Look at Exercise 12. Add to check your work.
Make a drawing to show the addition.

Solve Complex Word Problems

Write an equation. Solve the problem.

1 Marian has a collection of toy cars. She gives 28 cars to her brother Simon. Marian has 57 cars left. How many cars did she have to begin with?

☐ _____
                label

2 In September, Mr. Shaw planted some tulip bulbs. In October, he planted 35 more bulbs. Altogether he planted 81 bulbs. How many bulbs did he plant in September?

☐ _____
                label

3 Mrs. Lyle has a collection of 19 caps. She buys some more. Now she has 34 caps. How many caps did Mrs. Lyle buy?

☐ _____
                label

4 Tarik picks 41 flowers. He gives some of the flowers to his aunt. He has 24 flowers left. How many flowers did Tarik give to his aunt?

☐ _____
                label

Solve Complex Word Problems (continued)

Write an equation. Solve the problem.

5 Frank has some markers. He buys 15 more markers. Now he has 62 markers. How many markers did Frank have to begin with?

☐ _____
label

6 Kiki has 74 stickers. She gives some stickers to her friends. Now she has 29 stickers. How many stickers did Kiki give to her friends?

☐ _____
label

7 Miss Harrod has a jar with some seeds in it. She gives 53 seeds to the science teacher. There are 37 seeds left in the jar. How many seeds were in the jar before?

☐ _____
label

8 Josef has 59 sports cards. His friend Tara gives him some more cards. Now Josef has 78 sports cards. How many cards did Tara give him?

☐ _____
label

 Check Understanding

Write a completed equation that starts with 27 and has 93 as the total.

_____

Start Unknown Problems

Solve *Compare* Word Problems

Draw comparison bars and write an equation
to solve each problem.

1 Tia has 65 rocks. Stan has
29 rocks. How many more
rocks does Tia have than Stan?

☐ _____
       label

2 Dora has 27 fewer grapes
than Jerry. Jerry has
72 grapes. How many
grapes does Dora have?

☐ _____
       label

3 Lila has 34 toy trucks in her
collection, which is 18 fewer
than her friend Betty has.
How many toy trucks does
Betty have in her collection?

☐ _____
       label

4 One year the Ricos planted
97 flowers. This was 29 more
flowers than the Smiths planted.
How many flowers did the
Smiths plant?

☐ _____
       label

Solve *Compare* Word Problems (continued)

Draw comparison bars and write an equation
to solve each problem.

5 Pippa has 48 more beads than
Jeremy. Jeremy has 38 beads.
How many beads does Pippa
have?

☐ _____
          label

6 In the classroom, there are
25 fiction books and
64 nonfiction books. How
many fewer fiction books
than nonfiction books are in
the classroom?

☐ _____
          label

7 Boris has 16 more cherries than
Solongo. Boris has 60 cherries.
How many cherries does
Solongo have?

☐ _____
          label

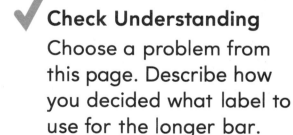

Check Understanding

Choose a problem from
this page. Describe how
you decided what label to
use for the longer bar.

Compare Word Problems

Name _____

Solve and Discuss

Make a drawing. Write an equation.
Solve.

---

1 Maxine's grandmother cuts out 48 fabric squares
to make a quilt. She needs 16 more squares to
complete the quilt. How many squares will be in
the quilt altogether?

[   ] _____
             label

---

2 Mr. Adams buys 93 paper plates for a party.
He buys 43 large plates. The rest are small.
How many small plates does he buy?

[   ] _____
             label

---

3 Henry collects shells. He has 32 shells. Jess gives him
some more shells. Now Henry has 51 shells. How
many shells did Jess give Henry?

[   ] _____
             label

---

4 Trina's team scores 56 points at the basketball game.
This is 30 more points than the other team scores.
How many points does the other team score?

[   ] _____
             label

      Mixed Word Problems **253**

Solve and Discuss (continued)

Make a drawing. Write an equation.
Solve.

5 Maura gives 19 trading cards to Jim. Now she has 24 trading cards. How many trading cards did Maura have to start?

_____
label

6 Jamal has 63 toy cars. Luis has 24 fewer toy cars than Jamal. How many toy cars does Luis have?

_____
label

7 Ms. Dow has some red balloons and some blue balloons. Altogether she has 46 balloons. How many balloons of each color could she have?

_____ and _____
label   label

8 Jon has 71 stickers. Ken has 53 stickers. How many fewer stickers does Ken have than Jon?

_____
label

Mixed Word Problems

Name _____

Solve and Discuss (continued)

Make a drawing. Write an equation.
Solve.

_____

9 Zoe has 22 more color pencils than Angelo.
Angelo has 38 color pencils. How many color
pencils does Zoe have?

[ ] _____
        label

_____

10 Nima is matching spoons and forks. She finds
36 spoons and 50 forks. How many more spoons
does Nima need to have the same number of
spoons as forks?

[ ] _____
        label

_____

11 Kirsty has some shells. Then she finds 24 more
shells at the beach. Now Kirsty has 100 shells.
How many shells did she start with?

[ ] _____
        label

_____

12 Landon has 84 beads. He uses some beads to
make a necklace. Now he has 45 beads left.
How many beads does Landon use to make
the necklace?

[ ] _____
        label

What's the Error?

Sona has 63 balloons. That is 16 more balloons than Molly. How many balloons does Molly have?

63 + 16 = 79
Sona   more   Molly

Did I make a mistake?

⑬ Draw comparison bars to help Puzzled Penguin. Write an equation to solve the problem.

Molly has ☐ balloons.

PATH to FLUENCY **Add and Subtract Within 100**

Add or subtract.

⑭   3 4
     + 4 6

⑮   1 3
     + 7 8

⑯   4 9
     + 2 6

⑰   9 5
     − 3 8

⑱   6 1
     − 2 8

⑲   6 0
     − 3 3

 Check Understanding

Choose a problem from page 245. Explain how your drawing and equation match the problem.

Mixed Word Problems

Name _____

Solve Two-Step Problems

Think about the first-step question.
Then solve the problem.

1   A farmer has two crates of milk bottles for sale.
    Each crate has 24 bottles. He sells 35 bottles.
    How many bottles of milk are left?

    ☐ _____
         label

2   There are 26 children at the library. 12 are girls and
    the rest are boys. Then 7 more boys come to the
    library. How many boys are at the library now?

    ☐ _____
         label

3   Jeff has 2 boxes of crayons and 15 other
    crayons. Each box contains 36 crayons.
    How many crayons does Jeff have altogether?

    ☐ _____
         label

Solve Two-Step Problems (continued)

Think about the first-step question.
Then solve the problem.

---

4 Lane collects 18 cans for recycling. Monette
collects 9 cans. Julia collects 12 more cans
than Lane and Monette collect together.
How many cans does Julia collect?

$\boxed{}$ _____
label

---

5 Fiona has 17 action figures. Logan has 9 more
action figures than Fiona. Bonnie has 12 fewer
action figures than Logan. How many action
figures does Bonnie have?

$\boxed{}$ _____
label

---

6 Mr. Tyson makes 75 rings to sell at a fair. He sells
16 rings on the first day. He sells some more on the
second day. Now he has 22 rings left. How many
rings did Mr. Tyson sell on the second day?

$\boxed{}$ _____
label

 Check Understanding

Draw the problem situation from Problem 5.

Two-Step Problems

Solve Two-Step Problems

Think about the first-step question.
Then solve the problem.

1 Lin gets $38 for babysitting. She spends $12 on
a present for her mother and puts the rest in a
money jar. She then gives some money to her
sister. Now Lin has $18 in her money jar.
How many dollars did Lin give her sister?

	_____

label

2 Russell has 28 marbles. Ridge has 12 fewer marbles
than Russell. Natasha has as many marbles as
Russell and Ridge together. How many marbles
does Natasha have?

	_____

label

3 Mr. Verdi is sewing costumes for the school play.
He needs 26 blue buttons. He also needs 16 green
buttons and 34 red buttons. How many buttons
does Mr. Verdi need in all?

	_____

label

Solve Two-Step Problems (continued)

Think about the first-step question.
Then solve the problem.

4 Mrs. Glover is sorting 56 feathers by color. 25 feathers
are red and the rest are green. Mrs. Glover adds some
more green feathers. Now she has 36 green feathers.
How many green feathers did Mrs. Glover add?

```
┌──────┐
│      │    _____
└──────┘
            label
```

5 Gabe and Juan find 32 leaves. Mari and Kaila find
12 more leaves than Gabe and Juan. If Mari finds
19 leaves, how many leaves does Kaila find?

```
┌──────┐
│      │    _____
└──────┘
            label
```

6 Kyle plants 15 seeds in the first pot. He plants 12 seeds
in the second pot and 18 seeds in the third pot. The
fourth pot is large. He plants as many seeds in the
fourth pot as in all the other three pots. How many
seeds does Kyle plant in the four pots altogether?

```
┌──────┐
│      │    _____
└──────┘
            label
```

✓ **Check Understanding**
Write the first-step question and answer for Problem 5.

_____

_____

　　　　　　　　　　　　More Two-Step Problems

Name _____

Make Measurements

The Stegosaurus was a large plant-eating dinosaur.
It had two rows of plates running along its back
and long spikes on its tail.

The feet of the Stegosaurus were short and wide.
The forefeet (the feet on the front legs) had
five short, wide toes with short hoof-like
tips. The rear feet had three short,
wide toes with hooves.

1. The rear foot of a Stegosaurus was about
   35 centimeters long. Use scissors and tape to make
   a paper strip that is 35 centimeters long. Write on
   the strip: *Foot of Stegosaurus.*

2. Now measure your own foot in centimeters.

   My foot is ☐ centimeters long.

   Make a paper strip that is the same length as your
   foot. Write on the strip: *My Foot.*

3. How much longer is the foot of the Stegosaurus
   than your foot?

   ☐ centimeters

Measure Stride

4 Work with a partner to measure your *stride*.

STEP 1. Put a piece of tape on the floor.

STEP 2. Line up your right and left heels with the edge of the tape.

STEP 3. Take a normal walking step with your left foot.

STEP 4. Take a normal walking step with your right foot.

STEP 5. Use tape to mark where the heel of your right foot lands.

STEP 6. Measure the distance in centimeters between the two pieces of tape. This is your *stride*.

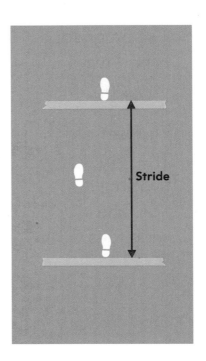

My stride is ⬚ centimeters long.

Make a paper strip that is the same length as your stride. Write on the strip: *My Stride.*

5 The stride of the Stegosaurus is measured using footprints from its right hind leg. Its stride was about 190 centimeters. Make a paper strip that is 190 centimeters long. Write on it: *Stride of Stegosaurus.*

6 How much longer is the stride of the Stegosaurus than your stride?

⬚ centimeters

7 Compare your stride with your partner's stride.

Who has the longer stride? _____

How much longer is it? ⬚ centimeters

Focus on Problem Solving

Name _____ Date _____

Solve.   **Show your work.**

1 Mrs. Rose buys 64 new pencils for her class.
She sharpens 23 of them in the morning.
She sharpens 22 of them in the afternoon.
How many pencils still need to be sharpened?

☐ _____
     label

---

2 Jill has 64 markers. Sam has 48 markers.
How many more markers does Jill have than Sam?

☐ _____
     label

---

3 Jeff has a collection of baseball cards.
He gives 36 baseball cards to his sister Clara.
Jeff has 39 baseball cards left.
How many baseball cards did he have at first?

☐ _____
     label

---

4 Clarissa has $1.00. She buys 2 pencils. Each pencil
costs 45¢. How much change should Clarissa get?

_____ ¢

Name _____ Date _____

Add or subtract.

1 7 + 9 = ☐   **2** 9 + 6 = ☐   **3** 13 + 5 = ☐

4 18 − 7 = ☐   **5** 13 − 5 = ☐   **6** 7 − 1 = ☐

7   24   **8**   39   **9**   67
        + 1 3   + 2 4   + 2 9

10   46   **11**   50   **12**   51
        −   9   − 1 5   − 3 8

13   94   **14**   1 0 0   **15**   91
        − 5 1   − 8 8   − 7 5

1 Subtract. Match each subtraction to its answer.

$$\begin{array}{r} 7\,4 \\ -\,3\,8 \\ \hline \end{array}$$ •

• 46

$$\begin{array}{r} 6\,3 \\ -\,1\,7 \\ \hline \end{array}$$ •

• 39

$91 - 52$ •

• 36

---

2 Is the answer correct? Choose Yes or No.

$$\begin{array}{r} 4\,7 \\ -\,1\,4 \\ \hline 2\,3 \end{array}$$ ○ Yes   ○ No

$$\begin{array}{r} 8\,7 \\ -\,5\,9 \\ \hline 2\,8 \end{array}$$ ○ Yes   ○ No

$$\begin{array}{r} 4\,1 \\ -\,1\,7 \\ \hline 2\,4 \end{array}$$ ○ Yes   ○ No

---

3 Hector has 1 dollar, 2 quarters, 1 dime, 3 nickels, and 1 penny.

Draw ☐100☐ s, ㉕ s, ⑩ s, ⑤ s, and ① s

to show his money.

Write the total amount of money. $ _____ . _____ _____
total

Under each picture, write the total amount of money so far. Then write the total using $.

4
| 25¢ | 25¢ | 25¢ | 10¢ | 10¢ | 10¢ |

25¢   50¢   _____   _____ _____ _____

$ _____ . _____ _____

total

Subtract.

5
$$\begin{array}{r} 100 \\ -\ 63 \\ \hline \end{array}$$

6
$$\begin{array}{r} 108 \\ -\ 29 \\ \hline \end{array}$$

---

7 Write a word problem to match the equation. Then solve.

$43 - 34 = \boxed{}$

_____

_____

_____

_____

Do you need to ungroup to subtract?
Choose Yes or No.

8
```
  I 4 0
-   8 9
```
○ Yes   ○ No

```
  2 0 0
-   5 4
```
○ Yes   ○ No

Solve.   **Show your work.**

9 Jaime, David, and Taylor have beads to make key
chains. Jaime has 24 beads. David has 12 more
beads than Jaime. Taylor has 14 fewer beads than
David. How many beads does Taylor have?

◻ _____
        label

---

10 Charlotte, Dustin, and Randy are picking
peaches. Charlotte picks 14 peaches, Dustin
picks 28 peaches, and Randy picks 23 peaches.
How many peaches do they pick?

◻ _____
        label

---

11 Jory has 2 large aquariums. They hold 28 fish and
44 fish. Round each number to the nearest 10.
About how many fish does Jory have?

about ◻ _____
               label

12 Brad subtracts 65 from 151. Should he follow
the steps listed below? Choose Yes or No.

Ungroup 5 tens as 4 tens 10 ones.	○ Yes	○ No
Subtract 5 ones from 10 ones.	○ Yes	○ No
Subtract 6 tens from 4 tens.	○ Yes	○ No
Subtract 6 tens from 14 tens.	○ Yes	○ No

13 Jeff wants to buy a baseball card for $1.52.
Show two ways he could pay for the baseball card.

☐ dollars ☐ quarters ☐ dimes

☐ nickels ☐ pennies

☐ dollars ☐ quarters ☐ dimes

☐ nickels ☐ pennies

14 Subtract 38 from 57. Explain all the steps you use.

$$\begin{array}{r} 57 \\ -38 \\ \hline \end{array}$$

The Fruit Stand

1 You have 2 quarters, 2 dimes, and 1 nickel.
Ring one fruit that you could buy from the fruit stand.

         🍌

56¢   47¢   83¢   39¢

Show the method you used to get the answer.

2 Draw coins to show the money you have left.
Use as few coins as possible.

3 Which fruit should you buy to have the greatest
amount of money left? Explain.

_____

_____

_____

Solve.

4 Nina has 8 dimes. She buys an apple. Does she
have enough money left to buy a banana? Explain.

_____

_____

_____

_____

5 Camilla has 1 dollar, 2 quarters, and 3 dimes.
Can she buy 2 pears and an apple? Explain.

_____

_____

_____

_____

6 Jacob has 2 quarters and 5 nickels. Cassie has 5 dimes
and 3 nickels. Who has enough money to buy an
apple? Explain.

_____

_____

_____

_____

Dear Family:

Your child is beginning a new unit on time.

You can help your child link the time concepts learned in school with the real world.

Together, look for clocks in your home. You might search for watches, alarm clocks, digital clocks, and clocks on appliances.

Talk about time throughout your family's day. For example, you can point to the clock during breakfast and say, "We usually eat breakfast at this time. It is 7:30 A.M."

In this unit, your child will learn to tell time to the hour, half hour, quarter-hour, and five minutes. Your child will practice writing the time.

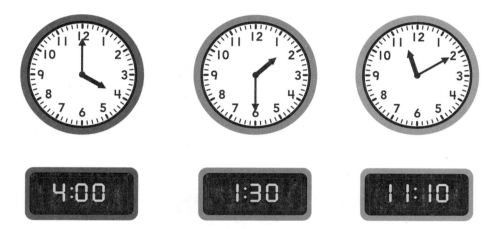

If you have any questions or comments, please contact me. Thank you.

Sincerely,
Your child's teacher

Estimada familia:

Su niño está empezando una unidad donde aprenderá sobre la hora.

Usted puede ayudarlo a que conecte los conceptos relacionados con la hora que aprendió en la escuela, con el mundo real.

Busquen juntos relojes en la casa. Puede buscar relojes de pulsera, relojes con alarma, relojes digitales y relojes que estén en los electrodomésticos.

Durante un día en familia, hablen de la hora. Por ejemplo, puede señalar un reloj durante el desayuno y decir: "Generalmente desayunamos a esta hora. Son las 7:30 a.m."

En esta unidad su niño aprenderá a leer la hora en punto, la media hora, cuarto de hora y los cinco minutos para la hora. Su niño practicará cómo escribir la hora.

Si tiene alguna pregunta o algún comentario, por favor comuníquese conmigo. Gracias.

Atentamente,
El maestro de su niño

A.M.

clock

analog clock

data

bar graph

digital clock

analog
clock

digital
clock

Use A.M. for times between midnight and noon.

	Sisters	Brothers
Kendra	2	1
Scott	2	0
Ida	0	1

data

The data in the table show how many sisters and how many brothers each child has.

Coins in My Collection

horizontal bar graph

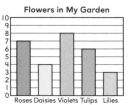

Flowers in My Garden

vertical bar graph

horizontal bar graph	picture graph
hour hand	P.M.
minute hand	quarter-hour

Apples	🍎🍎🍎🍎🍎🍎🍎
Oranges	⬤⬤⬤⬤⬤⬤⬤⬤⬤

Coins in My Collection

Use P.M. for times between noon and midnight.

hour hand

5 minutes
10 minutes
15 minutes

15 minutes = 1 quarter-hour

minute hand: points to the minutes

survey

tally chart

vertical bar
graph

When you collect data by asking people questions, you are taking a survey.

Our Favorite Pets

Pet	Tally	Number
Fish	IIII	4
Dogs	IIII IIII	10
Cats	IIII II	7

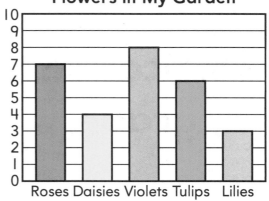

Flowers in My Garden

Features of Clocks

A **clock** is a tool that we use to measure time.

 Describe some clocks that you have seen.

_____

_____

_____

Write the missing numbers on each **analog clock**.

An analog clock has a long hand that is the **minute hand** and a short hand that is the **hour hand**.
Circle the hour hand on each clock.

Circle the minute hand on each clock.

Times of Daily Activities

VOCABULARY
A.M.
P.M.

We use **A.M.** for the hours after 12:00 midnight and before 12:00 noon.
  9:00 A.M. is 9 o'clock in the morning.
We use **P.M.** for the hours after 12:00 noon and before 12:00 midnight.
  9:00 P.M. is 9 o'clock in the evening.

11 Complete the chart. For each time listed, write whether it is dark or light outside; whether it is morning, afternoon, or evening; and an activity you might be doing at that time.

Time	Sunlight	Part of the Day	Activity
4:00 A.M.	dark	morning	sleeping
12:30 P.M.			
9:00 P.M.			

For each activity, circle the most appropriate time.

12 brush your teeth in the morning

  1:30 P.M.　　　3:00 P.M.　　　7:30 A.M.

13 eat dinner at night

  5:00 A.M.　　　12:00 noon　　　6:00 P.M.

14 watch an afternoon movie

  3:00 A.M.　　　2:00 P.M.　　　6:00 P.M.

Hours and A.M. or P.M.

Name _____

Model a Clock

Attach the clock hands using a prong fastener.

Paper Clock

Write Time

VOCABULARY
digital clock

On a **digital clock**, the number on the left shows the hour, and the number on the right shows the minutes after the hour.

hour   minutes

Write the time in two different ways.

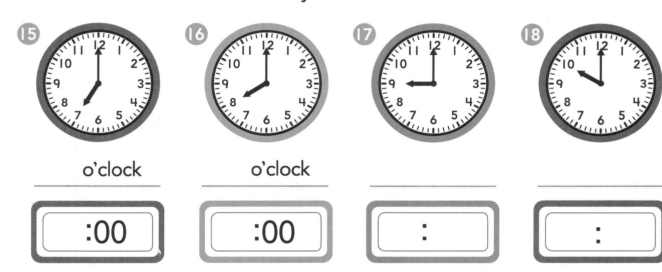

15 _____ o'clock

| :00 |

16 _____ o'clock

| :00 |

17 _____

| : |

18 _____

| : |

19 _____

| : |

20 _____

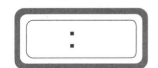

| : |

21 _____

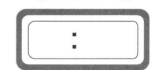

| : |

22 _____

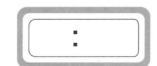

| : |

Draw Clock Hands

Draw the hands on each analog clock, and write the time on each digital clock below.

7 o'clock

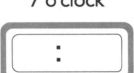

11 o'clock

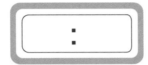

2 o'clock

3 o'clock

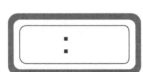

5 o'clock

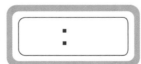

10 o'clock

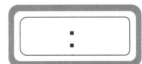

 Check Understanding

Show a time on your paper clock. Describe what you would do at that time if it were A.M. and if it were P.M.

Hours and A.M. or P.M.

Name _____

5-Minute Intervals

1 Count by 5s around the clock.

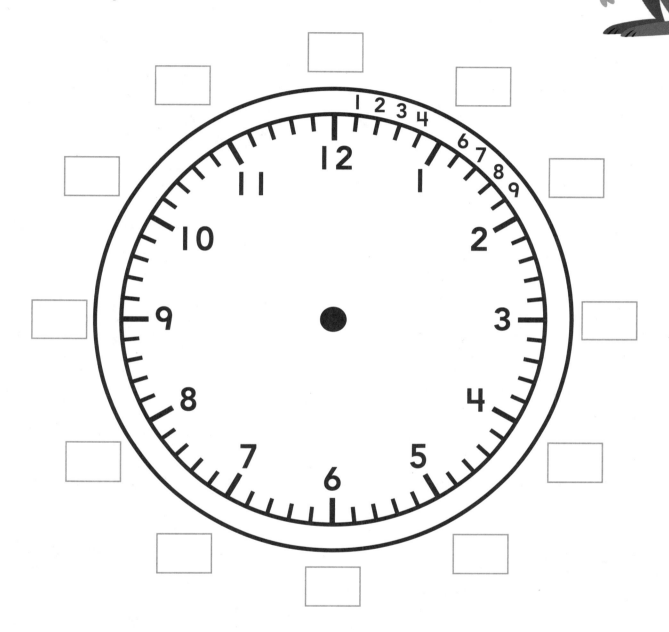

Read Time to 5 Minutes

Write the time on the digital clock.

2

3

4

5

6

7

8

9

10

11

12

13

© Houghton Mifflin Harcourt Publishing Company

Hours and Minutes

Name _____

Show Time to 5 Minutes

Draw hands on each clock to show the time.

10:35

9:20

2:45

4:50

7:05

3:30

5:50

8:00

10:15

12:25

3:55

4:30

What's the Error?

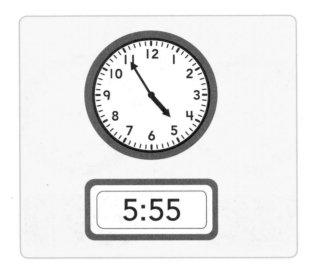

5:55

Did I make a mistake?

26 What is the correct time?

:

A.M. or P.M.?

For each activity, circle the appropriate time.

27 picnic

5:30 A.M.
5:30 P.M.

28 school recess

10:00 A.M.
10:00 P.M.

29 afternoon snack

3:15 A.M.
3:15 P.M.

30 going to the playground

9:25 A.M.
9:25 P.M.

31 lunch

12:10 A.M.
12:10 P.M.

32 sunset

7:05 A.M.
7:05 P.M.

33 wake up

6:45 A.M.
6:45 P.M.

34 math class

8:30 A.M.
8:30 P.M.

Hours and Minutes

Name _____

15-Minute Intervals

VOCABULARY
quarter-hour

35 Count by 15s around the clock.
Then use crayons to show each **quarter-hour**.
Make each quarter-hour a different color.

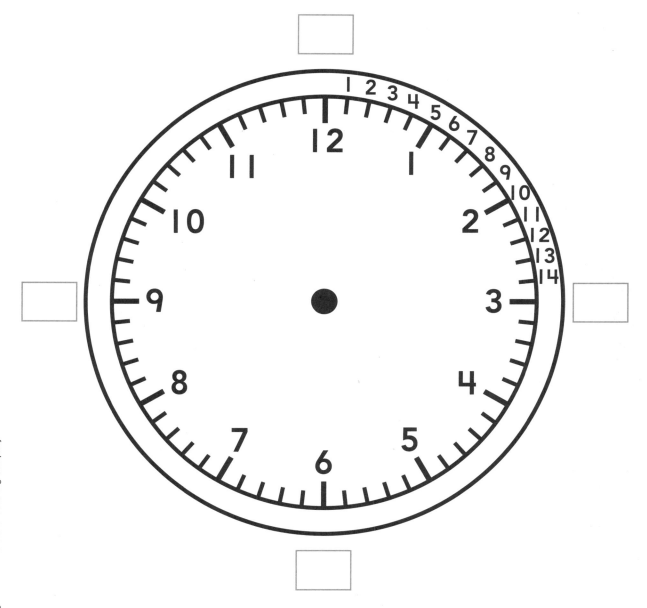

Hours and Minutes **283**

Tell Time to the Quarter-Hour

Write the time to the quarter-hour in different ways.

36

_____ o'clock

_____ : _____

37

_____ minutes after _____ o'clock

quarter after _____

_____ : _____

38

_____ minutes before _____ o'clock

quarter to _____

_____ : _____

39

_____ minutes after _____ o'clock

_____ : _____

40

_____ minutes before _____ o'clock

quarter to _____

_____ : _____

Hours and Minutes

Name _____

Understand Relationships of Time and the Calendar

Write the correct number.

41 I hour = [ ] minutes   **42** I day = [ ] hours

43 I week = [ ] days   **44** I minute = [ ] seconds

45 I year = [ ] weeks   **46** I year = [ ] days

47 I month = about [ ] weeks

Complete the names of the days of the week.

48 S̲u̲n̲d̲a̲y̲

M_____   T_____

T_____   F_____

W_____   S_____

Complete the following.

49 March has [ ] days.

Circle March 6 and March 16.

Put an X over every Saturday.

What day of the week is March 12?

_____

What day of the week is March 29?

_____

March						
S	M	T	W	T	F	S
				I	2	3
4	5	6	7	8	9	10
11	12	13	14	15	16	17
18	19	20	21	22	23	24
25	26	27	28	29	30	31

More Practice with Calendars

			January			
S	M	T	W	T	F	S
	1	2	3	4	5	6
7	8	9	10	11	12	13
14	15	16	17	18	19	20
21	22	23	24	25	26	27
28	29	30	31			

			February			
S	M	T	W	T	F	S
				1	2	3
4	5	6	7	8	9	10
11	12	13	14	15	16	17
18	19	20	21	22	23	24
25	26	27	28			

			March			
S	M	T	W	T	F	S
				1	2	3
4	5	6	7	8	9	10
11	12	13	14	15	16	17
18	19	20	21	22	23	24
25	26	27	28	29	30	31

			April			
S	M	T	W	T	F	S
1	2	3	4	5	6	7
8	9	10	11	12	13	14
15	16	17	18	19	20	21
22	23	24	25	26	27	28
29	30					

			May			
S	M	T	W	T	F	S
		1	2	3	4	5
6	7	8	9	10	11	12
13	14	15	16	17	18	19
20	21	22	23	24	25	26
27	28	29	30	31		

			June			
S	M	T	W	T	F	S
					1	2
3	4	5	6	7	8	9
10	11	12	13	14	15	16
17	18	19	20	21	22	23
24	25	26	27	28	29	30

			July			
S	M	T	W	T	F	S
1	2	3	4	5	6	7
8	9	10	11	12	13	14
15	16	17	18	19	20	21
22	23	24	25	26	27	28
29	30	31				

			August			
S	M	T	W	T	F	S
		1	2	3	4	
5	6	7	8	9	10	11
12	13	14	15	16	17	18
19	20	21	22	23	24	25
26	27	28	29	30	31	

			September			
S	M	T	W	T	F	S
						1
2	3	4	5	6	7	8
9	10	11	12	13	14	15
16	17	18	19	20	21	22
23	24	25	26	27	28	29
30						

			October			
S	M	T	W	T	F	S
	1	2	3	4	5	6
7	8	9	10	11	12	13
14	15	16	17	18	19	20
21	22	23	24	25	26	27
28	29	30	31			

			November			
S	M	T	W	T	F	S
				1	2	3
4	5	6	7	8	9	10
11	12	13	14	15	16	17
18	19	20	21	22	23	24
25	26	27	28	29	30	

			December			
S	M	T	W	T	F	S
						1
2	3	4	5	6	7	8
9	10	11	12	13	14	15
16	17	18	19	20	21	22
23	24	25	26	27	28	29
30	31					

50 How many months are in 1 year? ☐ months

51 Which months have 31 days? _____

_____

Which month has fewer than 30 days? _____

✔ **Check Understanding**
Circle the calendar months that only have 30 days.

1 For the activity, circle the time that makes sense.

eat dinner

6:30	A.M.	6:30	P.M.

---

2 Write the time on the digital clock.

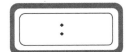

3 Draw hands on the clock to show the time.

6:05

Write the correct number.

4 1 hour = ☐ minutes

5 1 week = ☐ days

Name _____ Date _____

Add or subtract.

1 9 − 7 = ☐ **2** 15 − 5 = ☐ **3** 7 − 3 = ☐

4 7 + 4 = ☐ **5** 2 + 3 = ☐ **6** 6 + 8 = ☐

7
$$\begin{array}{r} 28 \\ -17 \\ \hline \end{array}$$

8
$$\begin{array}{r} 78 \\ -58 \\ \hline \end{array}$$

9
$$\begin{array}{r} 47 \\ -31 \\ \hline \end{array}$$

10
$$\begin{array}{r} 33 \\ +24 \\ \hline \end{array}$$

11
$$\begin{array}{r} 21 \\ +13 \\ \hline \end{array}$$

12
$$\begin{array}{r} 26 \\ +46 \\ \hline \end{array}$$

13
$$\begin{array}{r} 82 \\ -49 \\ \hline \end{array}$$

14
$$\begin{array}{r} 91 \\ -38 \\ \hline \end{array}$$

15
$$\begin{array}{r} 100 \\ -71 \\ \hline \end{array}$$

Dear Family:

Your child is learning how to show information in various ways. In this unit, children will learn how to create and read picture graphs, bar graphs, and tally charts.

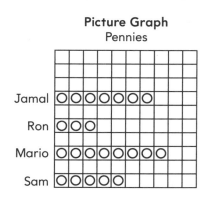

Picture Graph
Pennies

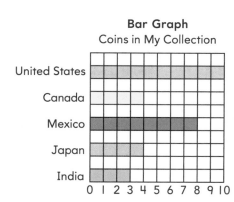

Bar Graph
Coins in My Collection

Tally Chart
Our Favorite Pets

Pet	Tally	Number
Fish	IIII	4
Dogs	IIII IIII	10
Cats	IIII II	7

An important feature of *Math Expressions* is its emphasis on real world connections. Children will collect and represent data on graphs. They will also interpret the graph to answer questions about the data shown.

Children also explore the language of comparison by using such words as *same, more, less,* and *fewer*. The connection between pairs of terms is emphasized. For example: Carlos has 8 stickers. Maria has 3. Carlos has 5 *more* stickers than Maria. Maria has 5 *fewer* stickers than Carlos has.

Please call if you have any questions or concerns. Thank you for helping your child learn how to create, read, and interpret graphs.

Sincerely,
Your child's teacher

Estimada familia:

Su niño está aprendiendo a mostrar información de varias maneras. En esta unidad los niños aprenderán a crear y a leer gráficas de dibujos, gráficas de barras y tablas de conteo.

Gráfica de dibujos
Monedas de 1 centavo

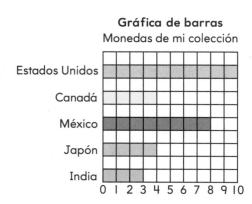

Gráfica de barras
Monedas de mi colección

Tabla de conteo

Nuestras mascotas favoritas

Mascota	Conteo	Número
Peces	IIII	4
Perros	IIIII IIIII	10
Gatos	IIIII II	7

Un aspecto importante de *Math Expressions* es su énfasis en las conexiones con situaciones de la vida cotidiana. Los niños reunirán datos y los representarán en gráficas. También interpretarán las gráficas para responder preguntas acerca de los datos que se muestran.

Los niños también estudiarán palabras que se usan para comparar, tales como *igual, mismo, más* y *menos*. Se hará énfasis en la conexión entre los pares de términos. Por ejemplo: Carlos tiene 8 adhesivos. María tiene 3. Carlos tiene 5 adhesivos *más* que María. María tiene 5 adhesivos *menos* que Carlos.

Si tiene alguna pregunta o algún comentario, por favor comuníquese conmigo. Gracias por ayudar a su niño a aprender cómo crear, leer e interpretar gráficas.

Atentamente,
El maestro de su niño

Name _____

Read to Make a Horizontal Picture Graph

Read the sentences below. Use the information
to make a horizontal picture graph.

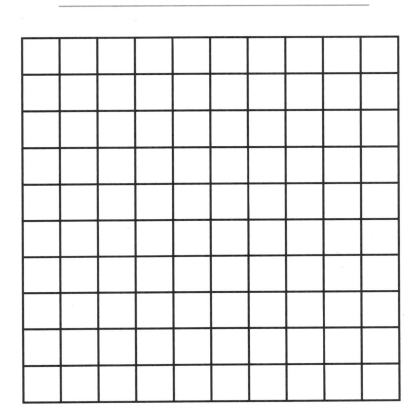

1 Miguel has 6 stickers.

2 Devin has 8 stickers.

3 Jennie has 4 stickers.

4 Hank has 3 stickers.

Discuss Picture Graphs **291**

Read to Make a Vertical Picture Graph

Read the sentences below. Use the information
to make a vertical picture graph.

_____

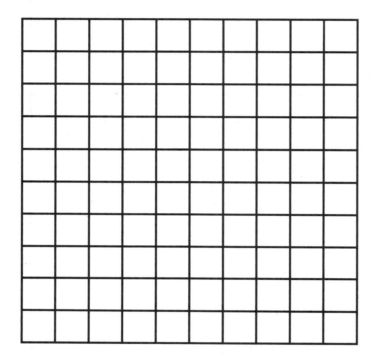

5 Carly has 2 comic books.

6 Dayo has 7 comic books.

7 Tomas has 5 comic books.

✔ Check Understanding

Shanice has 2 more comic books than Dayo. Add this
information to the vertical picture graph.

Discuss Picture Graphs

Name _____

Use Picture Graphs to Compare Amounts

Read the **picture graph**.

Write the number. Circle *more* or *fewer*.

Number of Balloons	
Carla	🎈🎈🎈🎈🎈🎈🎈
Peter	🎈🎈🎈🎈
Hanna	🎈🎈🎈🎈🎈

1 Carla has ☐ *more fewer* balloons than Peter.

2 Hanna has ☐ *more fewer* balloons than Carla.

_____

Read the picture graph. Write the number.

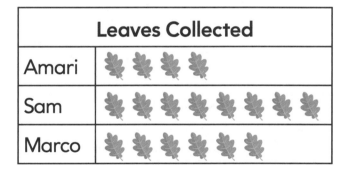

Leaves Collected	
Amari	🍂🍂🍂🍂
Sam	🍂🍂🍂🍂🍂🍂🍂
Marco	🍂🍂🍂🍂🍂

3 Amari needs ☐ more leaves to have as many as Sam has.

4 If Sam gives away ☐ leaves, he will have as many leaves as Marco has.

Solve *Put Together/Take Apart* Problems

This picture graph shows the number of apples Mrs. Reid bought at the store.

Apples Bought	
Red	🍎 🍎 🍎 🍎
Green	🍏 🍏
Yellow	🍏 🍏

5 How many apples did Mrs. Reid buy?

☐ _____
　　　label

6 There are 2 green apples, 1 yellow apple, and 1 red apple in the bowl. The rest are in Mrs. Reid's bag. How many apples are in the bag?

☐ _____
　　　label

This picture graph shows the number of books that four children read.

Books Read	
Pablo	📕 📕 📕
Janis	📕 📕
Helen	📕
Ray	📕 📕 📕 📕

7 Two children read 6 books altogether. Who are the two children?

_____ and _____

8 Two of the books the children read are about cars and 2 books are about trains. The rest of the books are about animals. How many books are about animals?

☐ _____
　　　label

✓ **Check Understanding**

How many more books would Janis need to read to equal the number of books Pablo and Ray read altogether? _____

Read Picture Graphs

Lori	🔲 🔲 🔲 🔲 🔲 🔲 🔲 🔲 🔲 🔲
Jessica	🔲 🔲 🔲 🔲 🔲 🔲
Erin	🔲 🔲 🔲 🔲 🔲 🔲 🔲 🔲

Use the picture graph. Write the number.
Circle *more* or *fewer*.

1 Erin has [ ] *more fewer* blocks than Jessica.

2 Jessica has [ ] *more fewer* blocks than Lori.

3 Lori has [ ] *more fewer* blocks than Erin.

Matthew	🐚 🐚 🐚 🐚
Cayden	🐚 🐚 🐚 🐚 🐚 🐚 🐚 🐚 🐚
John	🐚 🐚 🐚 🐚 🐚 🐚 🐚

Use the picture graph. Write the number.
Circle *more* or *fewer*.

4 Matthew has [ ] *more fewer* shells than Cayden.

5 Cayden has [ ] *more fewer* shells than John.

Name

Date

PATH to
FLUENCY

Add or subtract.

1 $5 + 3 = $ ☐   **2** $12 + 7 = $ ☐   **3** $8 + 5 = $ ☐

4 $12 - 4 = $ ☐   **5** $15 - 5 = $ ☐   **6** $15 - 9 = $ ☐

7
$$\begin{array}{r} 30 \\ +\ 10 \\ \hline \end{array}$$

8
$$\begin{array}{r} 41 \\ +\ 27 \\ \hline \end{array}$$

9
$$\begin{array}{r} 42 \\ +\ 14 \\ \hline \end{array}$$

10
$$\begin{array}{r} 54 \\ -\ 12 \\ \hline \end{array}$$

11
$$\begin{array}{r} 38 \\ -\ 20 \\ \hline \end{array}$$

12
$$\begin{array}{r} 67 \\ -\ 39 \\ \hline \end{array}$$

13
$$\begin{array}{r} 24 \\ +\ 58 \\ \hline \end{array}$$

14
$$\begin{array}{r} 46 \\ +\ 49 \\ \hline \end{array}$$

15
$$\begin{array}{r} 74 \\ +\ 26 \\ \hline \end{array}$$

Name _____

VOCABULARY
tally chart

Make a Tally Chart

1 Use the data to make a **tally chart**.

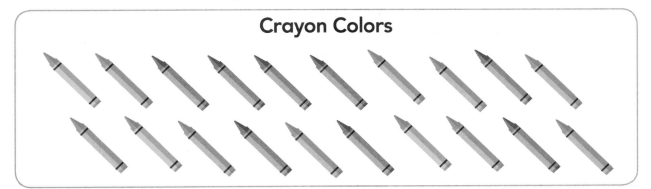

Crayon Colors

Title: _____

Color	Tally	Number
_____		
_____		
_____		

Use the tally chart to answer the questions.

2 How many fewer red crayons are there than blue crayons?

☐ _____
  label

3 There are 4 more yellow crayons than green crayons. Draw tally marks to show the number of yellow crayons.

Use a Tally Chart to Complete a Bar Graph

VOCABULARY
bar graph

4 Complete the tally chart.
Show that 3 more children chose cats than fish.

Our Favorite Pets

Pet	Tally	Number
Fish	IIII	4
Dogs	LHt LHt	10
Cats		

5 Use the tally chart to complete the **bar graph**.

Our Favorite Pets

Fish											
Dogs											
Cats											

0   1   2   3   4   5   6   7   8   9   10

Use the bar graph to answer the question.

6 How many children chose dogs or cats?

☐ _____
         label

Collect and Represent Data

Name _____

Make a Picture Graph

Title: _____

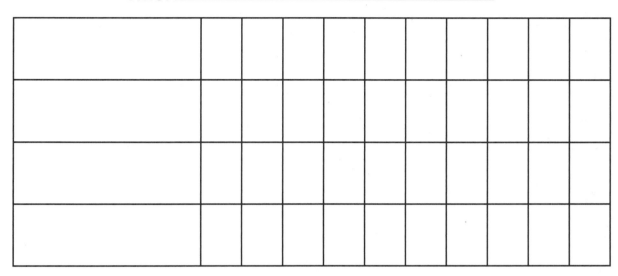

Make a Bar Graph

Title: _____

Collect and Represent Data **299**

(PATH to FLUENCY) Add and Subtract Within 100

Add.

⑦ $46 + 4 =$ _____   ⑧ $3 + 39 =$ _____   ⑨ $26 + 71 =$ _____

⑩
$$\begin{array}{r} 56 \\ + 36 \\ \hline \end{array}$$

⑪
$$\begin{array}{r} 11 \\ + 47 \\ \hline \end{array}$$

⑫
$$\begin{array}{r} 36 \\ + 53 \\ \hline \end{array}$$

⑬
$$\begin{array}{r} 78 \\ + 6 \\ \hline \end{array}$$

⑭
$$\begin{array}{r} 25 \\ + 61 \\ \hline \end{array}$$

⑮
$$\begin{array}{r} 18 \\ + 60 \\ \hline \end{array}$$

⑯
$$\begin{array}{r} 44 \\ + 17 \\ \hline \end{array}$$

⑰
$$\begin{array}{r} 13 \\ + 5 \\ \hline \end{array}$$

Subtract.

⑱ $74 - 8 =$ _____   ⑲ $51 - 12 =$ _____   ⑳ $60 - 15 =$ _____

㉑
$$\begin{array}{r} 42 \\ - 34 \\ \hline \end{array}$$

㉒
$$\begin{array}{r} 78 \\ - 29 \\ \hline \end{array}$$

㉓
$$\begin{array}{r} 43 \\ - 28 \\ \hline \end{array}$$

㉔
$$\begin{array}{r} 50 \\ - 18 \\ \hline \end{array}$$

㉕
$$\begin{array}{r} 80 \\ - 37 \\ \hline \end{array}$$

㉖
$$\begin{array}{r} 64 \\ - 45 \\ \hline \end{array}$$

㉗
$$\begin{array}{r} 28 \\ - 14 \\ \hline \end{array}$$

㉘
$$\begin{array}{r} 56 \\ - 27 \\ \hline \end{array}$$

 Check Understanding

Describe how bar graphs are different from picture graphs.

Collect and Represent Data

Name _____

VOCABULARY
horizontal bar graph
vertical bar graph

Read a Horizontal Bar Graph

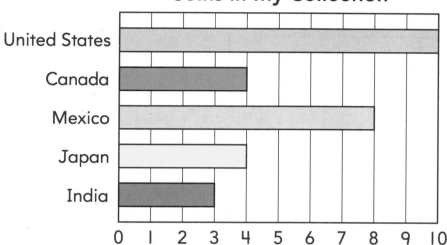

Coins in My Collection

United States
Canada
Mexico
Japan
India

0 1 2 3 4 5 6 7 8 9 10

Read a Vertical Bar Graph

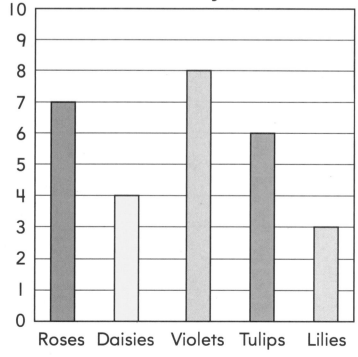

Flowers in My Garden

10
9
8
7
6
5
4
3
2
1
0

Roses Daisies Violets Tulips Lilies

Write Comparison Statements

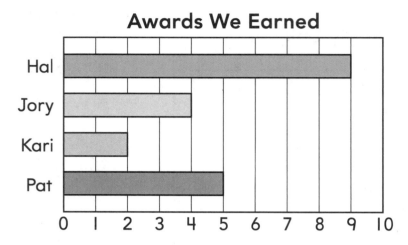

Awards We Earned

1. Use the horizontal bar graph.
   Write an *is greater than* statement.

_____

_____

Make a Vertical Bar Graph

2. Make a vertical bar graph
   from the horizontal
   bar graph above.

✓ **Check Understanding**
   Use the graph to write a
   comparison problem on
   your MathBoard. Trade
   problems with a partner
   and solve.

Read Bar Graphs

Name _____

Solve *Put Together/Take Apart* and *Compare* Problems

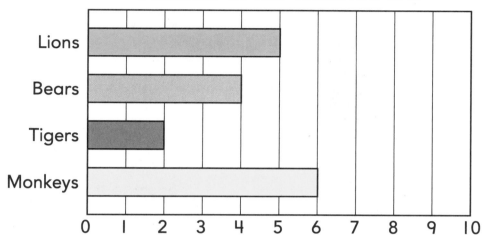

Animals at the Wildlife Park

Use the bar graph to solve the problems.   **Show your work.**

① Four of the monkeys are adults and the rest are babies. How many of the monkeys are babies?

[ ] _____
        label

② How many fewer bears are there than monkeys?

[ ] _____
        label

③ There are 2 fewer lions than elephants. How many elephants are there?

[ ] _____
        label

Solve Word Problems with More Than One Step

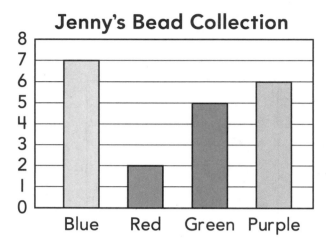

Jenny's Bead Collection

Use the bar graph to solve the problems.   **Show your work.**

4 Jenny has 4 fewer purple beads than Morgan. How many purple beads do Jenny and Morgan have in all?

◻ _____
         label

5 Morgan has 11 red beads. Then she gives 2 red beads to Arun. How many more red beads does Morgan have now than Jenny?

◻ _____
         label

6 Five of Jenny's beads are large and the rest are small. She buys some small yellow beads. Now she has 18 small beads. How many small yellow beads does she buy?

◻ _____
         label

Name _____

What's the Error?

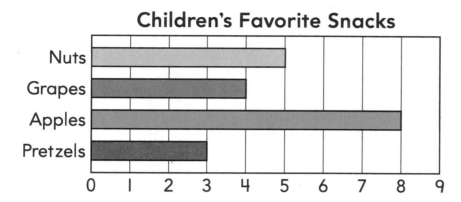

Children's Favorite Snacks

Nuts
Grapes
Apples
Pretzels

0 1 2 3 4 5 6 7 8 9

How many more children
choose fruit than nuts?

| Fruit | 8 |
| Nuts | 5 | ? |

$8 - 5 = 3$

3 more children

Am I correct?

7 Show Puzzled Penguin how you
would solve the problem.

[   ] more children

Organize and Graph Information

Here are some shapes for you to graph.

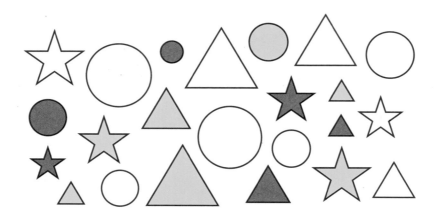

⑧ First make a table. ⑨ Then make a bar graph.

	Number

✓ **Check Understanding**
Explain another way that you could sort and graph the shapes. How many shapes would be in each group?

Solve Problems Using a Bar Graph

VOCABULARY
survey
data

Record the Collected Data

1 Show the results of your **survey** in the table. Your teacher will help you.

_____

_____	Number of Children

2 Show the **data** on a picture graph.

_____

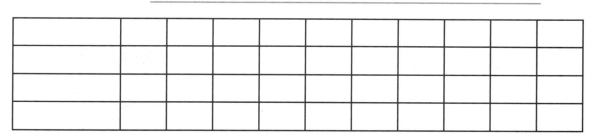

3 Show the data on a bar graph.

_____

4 Use the data to write a 2-step word problem.

_____

_____

© Houghton Mifflin Harcourt Publishing Company

What's the Error?

Favorite Subject	Number of Children
Reading	6
Math	7
Science	4
Art	4

Puzzled Penguin made a graph from the table.

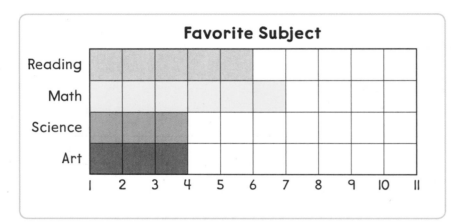

Did I make a mistake?

5 Fix Puzzled Penguin's errors.

PATH to FLUENCY Add and Subtract Within 100

Add or subtract.

6
$$\begin{array}{r} 76 \\ + 17 \\ \hline \end{array}$$

7
$$\begin{array}{r} 60 \\ - 37 \\ \hline \end{array}$$

8
$$\begin{array}{r} 12 \\ + 51 \\ \hline \end{array}$$

9
$$\begin{array}{r} 46 \\ - 19 \\ \hline \end{array}$$

✓ **Check Understanding**

When you take a survey, what are you doing?

_____

_____

　　　　Collect and Graph Data

Name _____

Make Graphs Using Data from a Table

The table shows the number of bicycles sold at a store on four days last week.

Bicycle Sales

Day	Number Sold
Saturday	8
Sunday	9
Monday	3
Tuesday	4

1 Make a picture graph using data from the table.

2 Make a bar graph using data from the table.

Solve Problems Using a Bar Graph

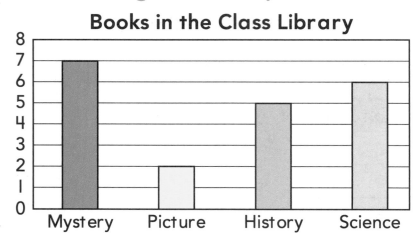

Books in the Class Library

Use the bar graph to solve the problems.　　　**Show your work.**

3 Children are reading 3 history books.
The rest are on the shelf in the library.
How many history books are on the shelf?

☐ _____
　　　label

4 The class library has 2 more science books than
math books. How many more math books must
the library get so there is the same number of
math books as mystery books?

☐ _____
　　　label

5 Children are reading some of the mystery books.
The rest are on the shelf. The library gets 6 new
mystery books. Now there are 10 mystery books on
the shelf. How many mystery books are children reading?

☐ _____
　　　label

　　　Make Graphs and Interpret Data

Name _____

Solve Problems Using a Bar Graph (continued)

Animals at a Farm

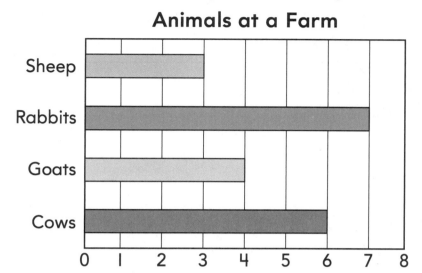

Use the bar graph to solve the problems.

Show your work.

6 The farm has 4 more rabbits than horses. How many horses does the farm have?

☐ _____
label

7 The farm has 5 fewer goats than chickens. How many chickens does the farm have?

☐ _____
label

8 There are 3 cows in the barn. The rest of the cows are in the field with the goats and the sheep. How many animals are in the field?

☐ _____
label

Solve *Compare* Problems with 2-Digit Numbers

Solve. Draw comparison bars for each.

9 A park has 46 maple trees. It has 18 fewer elm trees. How many elm trees are in the park?

☐ _____
            label

10 There are 62 pine trees in the park. There are 13 fewer pine trees than birch trees. How many birch trees are in the park?

☐ _____
            label

11 The park has 27 fir trees. There are 16 more spruce trees than fir trees. The park has 28 fewer spruce trees than oak trees. How many oak trees are in the park?

☐ _____
            label

✓ Check Understanding

Look at Problem 9. How many maple trees and elm trees are in the park altogether?

_____

Make Graphs and Interpret Data

Name _____

Make a Graph

Mrs. Pratt asks the children in her class to tell which kitten they think is the cutest of these four kittens.

 Fluffy

 Mink

 Odin

 Simba

The results of the survey are shown in this tally chart.

Which Kitten Do You Think Is the Cutest?

Fluffy	ⵏⵏⵏ I
Mink	IIII
Odin	ⵏⵏⵏ IIII
Simba	ⵏⵏⵏ I

1 Use the data in the tally chart to make a bar graph.

_____

_____

_____

_____

_____

Focus on Problem Solving **313**

Take a Survey

Your teacher will ask all of the children in the class to tell which puppy they think is the cutest of these four puppies.

| Romy | Parker | Domino | Bernie |

Show the results of the survey in this tally chart.

Which Puppy Do You Think Is the Cutest?

Romy	
Parker	
Domino	
Bernie	

2 Use the information in the tally chart to make a bar graph on your MathBoard.

3 Write a 2-step word problem that can be solved by using the bar graph. Trade problems with a classmate. Solve each other's problems.

_____

_____

_____

Use the picture graph.

①
Favorite Season

Winter	☺ ☺ ☺ ☺ ☺ ☺ ☺
Spring	☺ ☺ ☺ ☺
Summer	☺ ☺ ☺ ☺ ☺ ☺ ☺ ☺ ☺
Fall	☺ ☺ ☺ ☺ ☺

How many children voted in all?

_____
label

Use the bar graph to solve the problem.

② How many fewer children like red than blue?

[ ] _____
label

③ How many more children like yellow than green?

[ ] _____
label

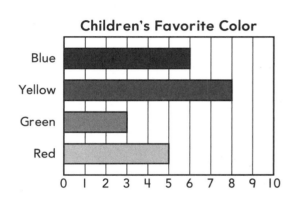

Children's Favorite Color

④ Make a bar graph to show the data in the table.

Math Awards

Grade	Number of Awards
First Grade	5
Second Grade	9
Third Grade	7
Fourth Grade	4

Name _____ Date _____

Add or subtract.

1 $8 - 7 =$ ☐ **2** $19 - 15 =$ ☐ **3** $7 - 6 =$ ☐

4 $7 + 8 =$ ☐ **5** $9 + 3 =$ ☐ **6** $10 + 10 =$ ☐

7
$$\begin{array}{r} 36 \\ -\ 14 \\ \hline \end{array}$$

8
$$\begin{array}{r} 60 \\ -\ 35 \\ \hline \end{array}$$

9
$$\begin{array}{r} 58 \\ -\ 23 \\ \hline \end{array}$$

10
$$\begin{array}{r} 44 \\ +\ 20 \\ \hline \end{array}$$

11
$$\begin{array}{r} 25 \\ +\ 24 \\ \hline \end{array}$$

12
$$\begin{array}{r} 17 \\ +\ 55 \\ \hline \end{array}$$

13
$$\begin{array}{r} 83 \\ -\ 68 \\ \hline \end{array}$$

14
$$\begin{array}{r} 58 \\ -\ 42 \\ \hline \end{array}$$

15
$$\begin{array}{r} 90 \\ -\ 29 \\ \hline \end{array}$$

Use the table.

Roses Picked

Child	Number Picked
Brad	7
Mark	9
Pam	8
Luis	5

1 Make a picture graph to show the data in the table.

_____

2 Make a bar graph to show the data in the table.

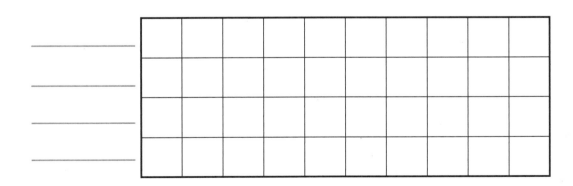

3 Use the picture graph. Choose the correct statements.

Strawberries									
Paula	🍓	🍓	🍓	🍓					
Reynaldo	🍓	🍓	🍓	🍓	🍓	🍓			

○ Paula has 2 more strawberries than Reynaldo.

○ Reynaldo has 2 more strawberries than Paula.

○ Paula and Reynaldo have 10 strawberries in all.

○ Reynaldo has 5 strawberries.

Use the bar graph to solve the problems.

4 The farm has 5 more goats than pigs. How many goats does the farm have?

☐ _____
    label

5 All of the horses and cows are in the pasture. Then 5 go back to the barn. Circle the number of animals that are still in the pasture.

| 10 |
| 11 | animals are in the pasture.
| 16 |

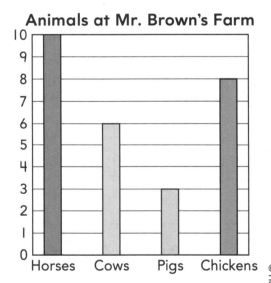

Animals at Mr. Brown's Farm

---

6 If Mr. Brown's farm gets 3 more pigs, how many more horses than pigs will there be?

☐ _____
    label

Use the bar graph.
Which statements are correct?
Choose Yes or No.

Colors of Flowers in Mrs. Singer's Garden

7 There are 3 more purple flowers than yellow flowers.

○ Yes   ○ No

8 There are 25 flowers in Mrs. Singer's garden in all.

○ Yes   ○ No

9 If 4 of the yellow flowers are tulips and the rest are daffodils, there must be 7 daffodils.

○ Yes   ○ No

10 Mrs. Singer plants 6 more orange flowers in her garden. Now there are 2 more orange flowers than red flowers.

○ Yes   ○ No

Circle the correct answer to complete the sentence.

11 At | 6:00 A.M. / 6:00 P.M. | , Joel watches the sunrise.

12 Owen has dinner at | 7:00 A.M. / 7:00 P.M. | .

13 There are | 12 / 24 | hours in 1 day.

Write the time on each digital clock.

⑭

⑮

⑯

⑰ The football game starts at 1:40. Draw hands on the clock to show the time.

Mac arrives at the football field at 1:55. Does he see the start of the game? Explain how you know.

_____

_____

_____

Solve. Draw comparison bars.

⑱ Elise picks 28 peaches. She picks 14 fewer than Charlie. How many peaches does Charlie pick?

☐ _____
      label

All in a Day

1 Terri, Kat, and Dana swim at 3:30. Show on
the clocks the time that they swim.

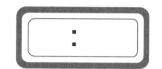

2 The table shows how many
days they swim in one
week. Make a picture graph
to show the data. Draw 1 circle
for each day. Then make a bar
graph to show the data.

Days Children Swim	
Terri	3
Kat	2
Dana	5

3 Write an *is greater than* statement about the data.
Write an *is less than* statement about the data.

_____

_____

_____

_____

Use the Days Children Swim graphs.
Complete each sentence.

4 Dana swims _____ more days than Terri.

5 Kat swims _____ fewer days than Dana.

6 Terri swims 1 _____ day than Kat.

7 Chad swims 4 days a week. Write a question that
compares the number of days Chad swims to the
number of days another child swims. Then solve.

_____

_____

_____

_____

Dear Family:

In this unit, children will learn how to add 3-digit numbers that have totals up to 1,000.

Children begin the unit by learning to count to 1,000. They count by ones from a number, over the hundred, and into the next hundred. For example, 498, 499, 500, 501, 502, 503. You can help your child practice counting aloud to 1,000. Listen carefully as he or she crosses over the hundred.

Children will learn to write numbers to 1,000. Some children will write 5003 instead of 503 for five hundred three. Using Secret Code Cards will help children write the numbers correctly.

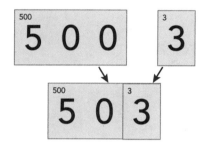

Help your child count small objects by making groups of 10 and then groups of 100. When the groups are made, help your child write the number of objects. This is a good way to help children recognize the difference between 5,003 and 503.

Please contact me if you have any questions or concerns. Thank you for helping your child learn about numbers to 1,000.

Sincerely,
Your child's teacher

Estimada familia:

En esta unidad los niños aprenderán cómo sumar números de 3 dígitos con totales de hasta 1,000.

Los niños comienzan la unidad aprendiendo a contar hasta 1,000. Cuentan de uno en uno a partir de un número, llegan a la centena y comienzan con la siguiente centena. Por ejemplo, 498, 499, 500, 501, 502, 503. Puede ayudar a su niño a practicar, contando en voz alta hasta 1,000. Ponga atención cada vez que llegue a una nueva centena.

Los niños aprenderán a escribir los números hasta 1,000. Tal vez, algunos niños escriban 5003 en vez de 503 al intentar escribir quinientos tres. Usar las Tarjetas de código secreto los ayudará a escribir correctamente los números.

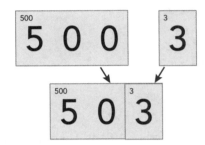

Ayude a su niño a contar objetos pequeños formando grupos de 10 y luego, grupos de 100. Cuando formen los grupos, ayúdelo a escribir el número de objetos. Esta es una buena manera de ayudar a los niños a reconocer la diferencia entre 5,003 y 503.

Si tiene alguna duda o pregunta, por favor comuníquese conmigo. Gracias por ayudar a su niño a aprender a contar hasta 1,000.

Atentamente,
El maestro de su niño

opposite
operations

ungroup

Addition and subtraction are opposite operations.

$$5 + 9 = 14$$
$$14 - 9 = 5$$

Use addition to check subtraction. Use subtraction to check addition.

$$\begin{array}{r} \overset{\overset{12}{0}\,\overset{2}{\cancel{3}}\,\overset{14}{\cancel{4}}}{\cancel{1}\cancel{3}\cancel{4}} \\ -\ 78 \\ \hline 56 \end{array}$$

Ungroup when you need more ones or tens to subtract.

Dollars with Penny Array (back)

Name _____

Represent 3-Digit Numbers

Write the number that is represented.

1

_____

_____

2

_____

_____

Draw boxes, sticks, and circles to represent the number.

3 164

_____

4 120

Represent 3-Digit Numbers (continued)

Write the number that is represented.

5  _____

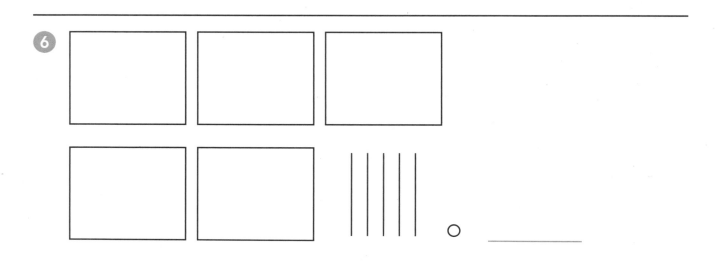 _____

Draw boxes, sticks, and circles to represent the number.

7 382

✓ **Check Understanding**

Ask a friend to name a 3-digit number.
Draw boxes, sticks, and circles to represent
that number.

© Houghton Mifflin Harcourt Publishing Company

Count Numbers to 1,000

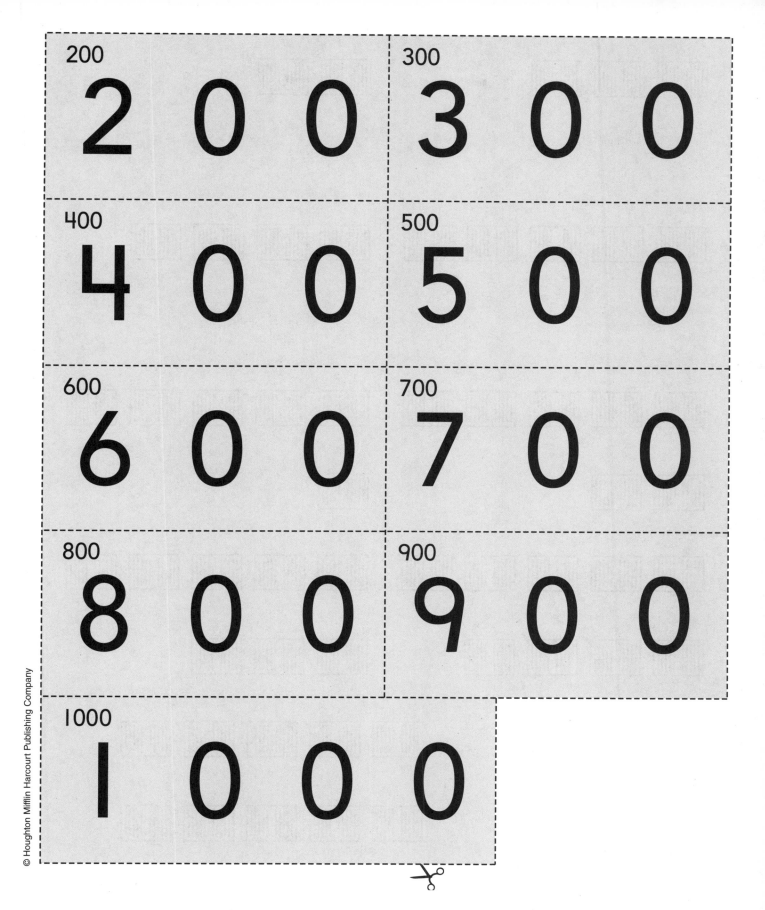

Secret Code Cards (200–1000) **329**

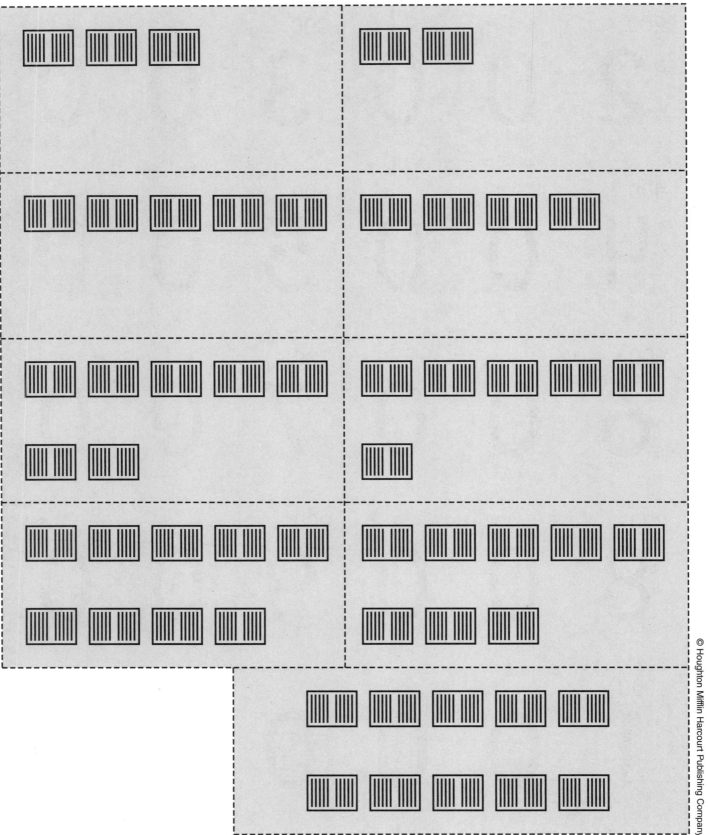

Secret Code Cards (200–1000)

Name _____

Review the Use of Boxes, Sticks, and Circles to Represent Numbers

Write the number that is shown by the drawing.

1 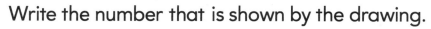 □□□□□ □ ||||| ||

_____   _____   _____   Total _____
Hundreds   Tens   Ones

2 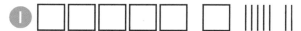 □□□ ||| °°°°°

_____   _____   _____   Total _____
Hundreds   Tens   Ones

3 □□□□ °°°°°
              °°°°

_____   _____   _____   Total _____
Hundreds   Tens   Ones

Draw boxes, sticks, and circles to show the number.

4 740

_____

5 876

_____

6 294

_____

7 502

Expanded Form

Write the hundreds, tens, and ones.

8 $382 = \underline{\ 300\ } + \underline{\ 80\ } + \underline{\ 2\ }$
   H T O

9 $738 = \underline{\quad} + \underline{\quad} + \underline{\quad}$

10 $526 = \underline{\quad} + \underline{\quad} + \underline{\quad}$

11 $267 = \underline{\quad} + \underline{\quad} + \underline{\quad}$

Write the number.

12 $400 + 50 + 9 = \underline{\ 459\ }$
                H T O

13 $800 + 10 + 3 = \underline{\quad}$

14 $100 + 70 + 5 = \underline{\quad}$

15 $600 + 40 + 1 = \underline{\quad}$

Write the number that makes the equation true.

16 $\underline{\quad} = 5 + 900 + 40$

17 $7 + 200 = \underline{\quad}$

18 $\underline{\quad} = 400 + 6 + 80$

19 $800 + 40 = \underline{\quad}$

20 $\underline{\quad} = 70 + 300$

21 $60 + 500 + 3 = \underline{\quad}$

22 $\underline{\quad} = 2 + 400$

23 $9 + 90 + 200 = \underline{\quad}$

24 $462 = 2 + 400 + \underline{\quad}$

25 $\underline{\quad} + 90 + 700 = 798$

26 $523 = 20 + 3 + \underline{\quad}$

27 $\underline{\quad} + 4 + 200 = 224$

✓ **Check Understanding**

Describe how the Secret Code Cards can be used to show the expanded form of a number.

        Place Value

Solve and Discuss

Write <, >, or =.

1 635 ◯ 735

2 527 ◯ 527

3 820 ◯ 518

4 327 ◯ 372

5 975 ◯ 987

6 321 ◯ 567

7 267 ◯ 267

8 271 ◯ 172

9 654 ◯ 564

10 750 ◯ 507

Write the numbers in order from least to greatest.

11 278   528   142

___   ___   ___
least   greatest

12 739   391   826

___   ___   ___
least   greatest

13 408   653   294

___   ___   ___
least   greatest

14 935   953   539

___   ___   ___
least   greatest

Compare and Order Numbers

Write <, >, or =.

⑮ 620 ◯ 62

⑯ 510 ◯ 150

⑰ 71 ◯ 315

⑱ 357 ◯ 218

⑲ 359 ◯ 359

⑳ 376 ◯ 476

Write the numbers in order from greatest to least.

㉑ 452   718   637

____   ____   ____
greatest   least

㉒ 338   501   332

____   ____   ____
greatest   least

㉓ 834   143   745   790   226   624

____   ____   ____   ____   ____   ____
greatest   least

PATH to FLUENCY Add or Subtract Within 100

Add or subtract.

㉔   1 9
   + 6 0
   _____

㉕   2 7
   + 7 3
   _____

㉖   9 8
   − 3 5
   _____

㉗   8 3
   − 7 8
   _____

 Check Understanding

Explain how to compare 728 and 723.

Compare and Order Numbers Within 999

Name _____

Count Over a Hundred by Ones and by Tens

Count by ones. Write the numbers.

1 396 397 _398_ _399_ _400_ _401_ _402_ _403_ 404

2 594 595 ___ ___ ___ ___ ___ ___ 602

3 297 298 ___ ___ ___ ___ ___ ___ 305

4 495 ___ ___ ___ ___ ___ ___ ___ 503

5 598 ___ ___ ___ ___ ___ ___ ___ 606

6 697 ___ ___ ___ ___ ___ ___ ___ 705

Count by tens. Write the numbers.

7 460 470 _480_ _490_ _500_ _510_ _520_ _530_ 540

8 370 380 ___ ___ ___ ___ ___ ___ 450

9 640 650 ___ ___ ___ ___ ___ ___ 720

10 580 ___ ___ ___ ___ ___ ___ ___ 660

11 750 ___ ___ ___ ___ ___ ___ ___ 830

12 830 ___ ___ ___ ___ ___ ___ ___ 910

Read and Write Number Names

You can write numbers with words or symbols.

1 one	11 eleven	10 ten	100 one hundred
2 two	12 twelve	20 twenty	200 two hundred
3 three	13 thirteen	30 thirty	300 three hundred
4 four	14 fourteen	40 forty	400 four hundred
5 five	15 fifteen	50 fifty	500 five hundred
6 six	16 sixteen	60 sixty	600 six hundred
7 seven	17 seventeen	70 seventy	700 seven hundred
8 eight	18 eighteen	80 eighty	800 eight hundred
9 nine	19 nineteen	90 ninety	900 nine hundred
			1,000 one thousand

Write each number.

13 one hundred twenty-five _____   14 four hundred fifty-eight _____

15 six hundred thirty-one _____   16 nine hundred sixty-two _____

17 eight hundred forty _____   18 seven hundred three _____

Write each number name.

19 500 _____

20 650 _____

21 605 _____

22 1,000 _____

✓ **Check Understanding**

Write a 3-digit number. Trade with a friend. Write the number name for your friend's 3-digit number.

Count by Ones and by Tens

Name _____

Add Numbers with 1, 2, and 3 Digits

Solve.

1 $200 + 200 =$ _____ $200 + 20 =$ _____ $200 + 2 =$ _____

$300 + 300 =$ _____ $300 + 30 =$ _____ $300 + 3 =$ _____

$400 + 400 =$ _____ $400 + 40 =$ _____ $400 + 4 =$ _____

$500 + 500 =$ _____ $500 + 50 =$ _____ $500 + 5 =$ _____

---

2 $600 + 200 =$ _____ $20 + 600 =$ _____ $2 + 600 =$ _____

$700 + 300 =$ _____ $30 + 700 =$ _____ $3 + 700 =$ _____

$800 + 100 =$ _____ $10 + 800 =$ _____ $1 + 800 =$ _____

$900 + 100 =$ _____ $10 + 900 =$ _____ $1 + 900 =$ _____

$100 + 900 =$ _____ $90 + 100 =$ _____ $9 + 100 =$ _____

---

3 $100 + 134 =$ _____ $100 + 34 =$ _____ $4 + 100 =$ _____

$200 + 245 =$ _____ $200 + 45 =$ _____ $200 + 5 =$ _____

$300 + 356 =$ _____ $56 + 300 =$ _____ $6 + 300 =$ _____

$400 + 467 =$ _____ $400 + 67 =$ _____ $400 + 7 =$ _____

$500 + 478 =$ _____ $78 + 500 =$ _____ $8 + 500 =$ _____

Add Ones, Tens, and Hundreds **337**

Solve and Discuss

Solve each word problem. Use Secret Code Cards
or make proof drawings if you wish.

4 A camping club buys some bags
of raisins. They buy 3 cartons
that have 100 bags each. They
also have 24 bags left from their
last trip. How many bags of
raisins does the club have?

[ ] _____
label

5 Two friends want to make
necklaces. They buy 1 package
of one hundred red beads,
1 package of one hundred blue
beads, and 1 package of
one hundred green beads.
They already have 12 loose
beads. How many beads do
they have altogether?

[ ] _____
label

6 All of the students at a school
go out on the playground.
They form 6 groups of one
hundred students and 5 groups
of ten students. There are
8 students left. How many
students go to the school?

[ ] _____
label

 Check Understanding

Solve.

$4 +$
two hundred $+$
3 groups of ten $=$ [ ]

Add Ones, Tens, and Hundreds

Name _____ Date _____

Count the hundreds, tens, and ones.
Then write the total.

1 ||||| |||| °°°°°

_____ _____ _____   Total _____
Hundreds Tens   Ones

Write the hundreds, tens, and ones.
Then write the number name.

2 749 = ____ + ____ + ____

_____

Write <, >, or =.

3 641 ◯ 614

Count by 10s. Write the numbers.

4 370 380 ____ ____ ____ ____ ____ ____ 450

Solve.   **Show your work.**

5 Victor bought some stickers. He bought
3 pages that had 100 stickers on each
page. He also bought 27 extra stickers.
How many stickers did he buy in all?

┌──────┐ _____
│   │   label
└──────┘

Name _____

Date _____

Add or subtract.

1 $19 - 6 =$ ☐   **2** $12 - 3 =$ ☐   **3** $7 - 2 =$ ☐

4 $10 + 10 =$ ☐   **5** $14 + 3 =$ ☐   **6** $8 + 2 =$ ☐

7
$$\begin{array}{r} 31 \\ -20 \\ \hline \end{array}$$

8
$$\begin{array}{r} 58 \\ -49 \\ \hline \end{array}$$

9
$$\begin{array}{r} 36 \\ -\ 2 \\ \hline \end{array}$$

10
$$\begin{array}{r} 54 \\ +37 \\ \hline \end{array}$$

11
$$\begin{array}{r} 15 \\ +34 \\ \hline \end{array}$$

12
$$\begin{array}{r} 29 \\ +57 \\ \hline \end{array}$$

13
$$\begin{array}{r} 86 \\ -58 \\ \hline \end{array}$$

14
$$\begin{array}{r} 100 \\ -\ 47 \\ \hline \end{array}$$

15
$$\begin{array}{r} 95 \\ -39 \\ \hline \end{array}$$

Dear Family:

Your child is now learning how to add 3-digit numbers. The methods children use are similar to those used for adding 2-digit numbers.

New Groups Below

Step 1

$$456 + 278$$
4

Step 2

$$456 + 278$$
34

Step 3

$$456 + 278$$
734

400   100   10
200

Children put the new 1 hundred or 1 ten on the line instead of at the top of the column. Many children find this less confusing because:

- They can see the 14.
- It is easier to add the 1 after they add the 5 and the 7.

Show All Totals

$$456 + 278$$

hundreds → 600
tens → 120
ones → 14
734

Children see the hundreds, tens, and ones they are adding. These can also be seen when they make a math drawing like the one above.

Children may use any method that they understand, can explain, and can do fairly quickly. They should use hundreds, tens, and ones language to explain. This shows that they understand that they are adding 4 hundreds and 2 hundreds, not 4 and 2.

Please contact me if you have questions or comments.

Sincerely,
Your child's teacher

Estimada familia:

Ahora su niño está aprendiendo a sumar números de 3 dígitos. Los métodos que los niños usarán son semejantes a los usados para sumar numeros de 2 dígitos.

Grupos nuevos abajo

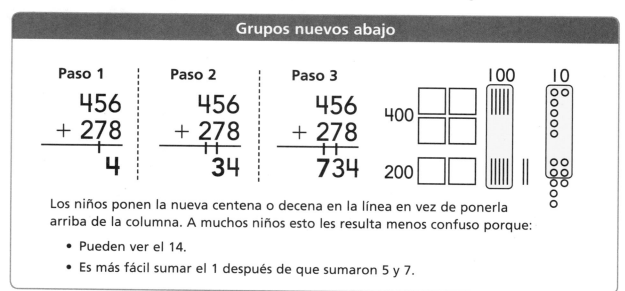

Paso 1	Paso 2	Paso 3
456	456	456
+ 278	+ 278	+ 278
4	34	734

Los niños ponen la nueva centena o decena en la línea en vez de ponerla arriba de la columna. A muchos niños esto les resulta menos confuso porque:

- Pueden ver el 14.
- Es más fácil sumar el 1 después de que sumaron 5 y 7.

Mostrar todos los totales

```
        456
      + 278
centenas → 600
 decenas → 120
unidades →  14
        734
```

Los niños ven las centenas, las decenas y las unidades que están sumando. Esto también se puede observar cuando hacen un dibujo matemático como el de arriba.

Los niños pueden usar cualquier método que comprendan, puedan explicar y puedan hacer relativamente rápido. Para explicar deben usar un lenguaje relacionado con centenas, decenas y unidades. Esto demuestra que entienden que están sumando 4 centenas y 2 centenas, no 4 y 2.

Si tiene alguna duda o pregunta, por favor comuníquese conmigo.

Atentamente,
El maestro de su niño

3-Digit Addition

Solve and Discuss

Solve each word problem.
Be ready to explain what you did.

1. Mrs. Ruth makes a display of plant and fish fossils for the library. She puts in 478 plant fossils. She puts in 67 fish fossils. How many fossils are in the display?

[ ] _____
label

2. The members of the nature club planted pine and birch trees this year. There were 496 birch trees planted and 283 pine trees planted. How many pine and birch trees were planted in all?

[ ] _____
label

3. There are 818 ducks entered in the Rubber Duck River Race. Then 182 more are added. How many ducks are in the race now?

[ ] _____
label

4. There are 189 children at Camp Sunshine. There are 375 children at Camp Bluebird. How many children are there at the two camps?

[ ] _____
label

Practice 3-Digit Addition

Add using any method. Make a proof drawing if it helps.

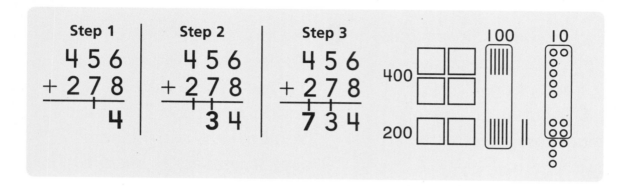

5   375
   +482

6   148
   +236

7   584
   + 61

8   168
   +674

9   89
   +376

10   563
   +157

11   497
   +259

12   124
   +563

13   348
   +239

✓ Check Understanding

Make a proof drawing for Exercise 11.

Name _____

New Ten or New Hundred

Add. Use any method. Make a proof drawing if it helps.

①
```
   2 3 6
 + 4 7 8
```

Make a new ten? _____

Make a new hundred? _____

② $183 + 517 =$ _____

Make a new ten? _____

Make a new hundred? _____

③ $93 + 485 =$ _____

Make a new ten? _____

Make a new hundred? _____

④
```
   3 6 8
 + 2 5 7
```

Make a new ten? _____

Make a new hundred? _____

⑤ $347 + 37 =$ _____

Make a new ten? _____

Make a new hundred? _____

⑥ $645 + 87 =$ _____

Make a new ten? _____

Make a new hundred? _____

Discuss 3-Digit Addition **345**

New Ten, New Hundred, or New Thousand

Add. Use any method. Draw a proof drawing if it helps.

7
$$\begin{array}{r} 195 \\ +172 \\ \hline \end{array}$$

Make a new ten? _____

Make a new hundred? _____

Make a new thousand? _____

8
$$\begin{array}{r} 300 \\ +700 \\ \hline \end{array}$$

Make a new ten? _____

Make a new hundred? _____

Make a new thousand? _____

9 360 + 640 = _____

Make a new ten? _____

Make a new hundred? _____

Make a new thousand? _____

10 75 + 823 = _____

Make a new ten? _____

Make a new hundred? _____

Make a new thousand? _____

11 905 + 95 = _____

Make a new ten? _____

Make a new hundred? _____

Make a new thousand? _____

12 413 + 587 = _____

Make a new ten? _____

Make a new hundred? _____

Make a new thousand? _____

 Check Understanding

Explain how you found the sum for Exercise 9.

Discuss 3-Digit Addition

Find the Hidden Animal

Directions for the puzzle on page 348:

- Find one of the sums below. Then look for that sum in the puzzle grid. Color in that puzzle piece.

- Find all 20 sums. Color the puzzle pieces with the sums. Color in all 20 correct answers.

- Name the hidden animal. It is a(n) _____.

$$
\begin{array}{r} 524 \\ + 247 \\ \hline \end{array}
\qquad
\begin{array}{r} 287 \\ + 164 \\ \hline \end{array}
\qquad
\begin{array}{r} 384 \\ + 375 \\ \hline \end{array}
\qquad
\begin{array}{r} 456 \\ + 174 \\ \hline \end{array}
\qquad
\begin{array}{r} 327 \\ + 265 \\ \hline \end{array}
$$

$$
\begin{array}{r} 207 \\ + 595 \\ \hline \end{array}
\qquad
\begin{array}{r} 248 \\ + 376 \\ \hline \end{array}
\qquad
\begin{array}{r} 282 \\ + 457 \\ \hline \end{array}
\qquad
\begin{array}{r} 548 \\ + 387 \\ \hline \end{array}
\qquad
\begin{array}{r} 233 \\ + 288 \\ \hline \end{array}
$$

$$
\begin{array}{r} 367 \\ + 265 \\ \hline \end{array}
\qquad
\begin{array}{r} 293 \\ + 595 \\ \hline \end{array}
\qquad
\begin{array}{r} 284 \\ + 376 \\ \hline \end{array}
\qquad
\begin{array}{r} 537 \\ + 463 \\ \hline \end{array}
\qquad
\begin{array}{r} 138 \\ + 327 \\ \hline \end{array}
$$

$$
\begin{array}{r} 286 \\ + 78 \\ \hline \end{array}
\qquad
\begin{array}{r} 407 \\ + 266 \\ \hline \end{array}
\qquad
\begin{array}{r} 503 \\ + 148 \\ \hline \end{array}
\qquad
\begin{array}{r} 78 \\ + 65 \\ \hline \end{array}
\qquad
\begin{array}{r} 192 \\ + 339 \\ \hline \end{array}
$$

© Houghton Mifflin Harcourt Publishing Company

See page 347 for directions on how to solve the puzzle.

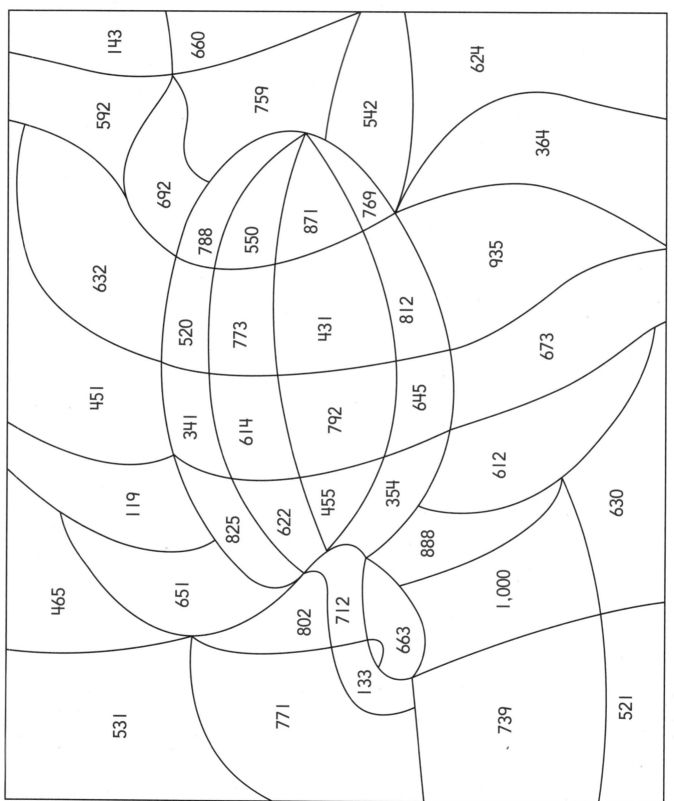

Discuss 3-Digit Addition

Name _____

Adding Up to Solve Word Problems

Solve each word problem.   **Show your work.**

① Mr. Cruz has 750 yams to sell. He sells
some and has 278 yams left. How many
yams does he sell?

☐ _____
        label

② At the end of February there are 692 houses
in our town. Some new houses are built in
March. At the end of March there are 976 houses.
How many houses are built in March?

☐ _____
        label

③ Delia has 224 shells in her collection. She gives
some to her sister. Now she has 162 shells.
How many shells did she give away?

☐ _____
        label

④ On Saturday, 703 people go to a movie.
194 go in the afternoon. The rest go in
the evening. How many people go to the
movie in the evening?

☐ _____
        label

Adding Up to Solve Word Problems (continued)

Solve.   **Show your work.**

⑤ Mr. Kelley makes 525 coasters that are circles or squares to sell at the art fair. 347 coasters are circles. How many coasters are squares?

```
┌───────┐    _____
│       │
└───────┘            label
```

PATH to FLUENCY Add and Subtract Within 100

Add.

⑥   3 2   ⑦   4 2   ⑧   5 7   ⑨   4 4
    + 5 0   + 5 7   + 4 3   +   7

Subtract.

⑩   9 8   ⑪   1 0 0   ⑫   4 3   ⑬   6 1
    − 2 4   −   3 1   − 3 8   − 2 9

✔ **Check Understanding**

Use the Adding Up Method to solve.

$251 + \boxed{} = 632$

$251 + \underline{} = 260$

$260 + \underline{} = 300$

$300 + \underline{} = 600$

$600 + \underline{} = 632$

$251 + \boxed{} = 632$

Add.

1   3 1 8
   +2 5 3

2   4 8 6
   +3 5 7

Solve.   Show your work.

3 Mrs. Green drives 357 miles on Monday and 292 miles
   on Tuesday. How many miles does she drive in all?

   ☐ _____
          label

4 Mrs. Brach made 400 quilts to sell. After she sold some,
   she had 174 left. How many quilts did she sell?

   ☐ _____
          label

5 On Friday, 834 meals were served. 458 meals were
   served at breakfast. The rest were served at lunch.
   How many meals were served at lunch?

   ☐ _____
          label

Name _____

Date _____

PATH to
FLUENCY

Add or subtract.

1 $15 - 8 =$ ☐

2 $16 - 13 =$ ☐

3 $14 - 4 =$ ☐

4 $8 + 9 =$ ☐

5 $11 + 6 =$ ☐

6 $9 + 11 =$ ☐

7
$$\begin{array}{r} 26 \\ -5 \\ \hline \end{array}$$

8
$$\begin{array}{r} 56 \\ +42 \\ \hline \end{array}$$

9
$$\begin{array}{r} 26 \\ -13 \\ \hline \end{array}$$

10
$$\begin{array}{r} 70 \\ -63 \\ \hline \end{array}$$

11
$$\begin{array}{r} 30 \\ +48 \\ \hline \end{array}$$

12
$$\begin{array}{r} 29 \\ +25 \\ \hline \end{array}$$

13
$$\begin{array}{r} 57 \\ +43 \\ \hline \end{array}$$

14
$$\begin{array}{r} 23 \\ +68 \\ \hline \end{array}$$

15
$$\begin{array}{r} 38 \\ +37 \\ \hline \end{array}$$

Dear Family:

Your child is now learning how to subtract 3-digit numbers. The most important part is understanding and being able to explain a method. Children may use any method that they understand, can explain, and can perform fairly quickly.

Expanded Method

Step 1   Step 2

$$432 = 400 + 30 + 2 = \overset{300}{\cancel{400}} + \overset{\overset{120}{\cancel{20}}}{\cancel{30}} + \overset{12}{\cancel{2}}$$
$$- 273 = 200 + 70 + 3 = 200 + 70 + 3$$

Step 3 $\begin{cases} 100 + 50 + 9 \\ = 159 \end{cases}$

Step 1 "Expand" each number to show that it is made up of hundreds, tens, and ones.

Step 2 Check to see if there are enough ones to subtract from. If not, ungroup a ten into 10 ones and add it to the existing ones. Check to see if there are enough tens to subtract from. If not, ungroup a hundred into 10 tens and add it to the existing tens. Children may also ungroup from the left.

Step 3 Subtract to find the answer. Children may subtract from left to right or right to left.

Ungroup First Method

Step 1 Check to see if there are enough ones and tens to subtract from. Ungroup where needed.

Look inside 432. Ungroup 432 and rename it as 3 hundreds, 12 tens, and 12 ones.

Ungroup from the left:

Ungroup from the right:

Step 2 Subtract to find the answer. Children may subtract from the left or from the right.

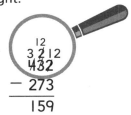

In explaining any method they use, children are expected to use "hundreds, tens, and ones" language and drawings to show that they understand place value.

Please contact me if you have questions or comments.

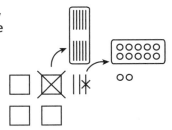

Sincerely,
Your child's teacher

Estimada familia:

Su niño está aprendiendo a restar números de 3 dígitos. Lo más importante es comprender y saber explicar un método. Los niños pueden usar cualquier método que comprendan, puedan explicar y puedan hacer relativamente rápido.

Método extendido

Paso 1   **Paso 2**

$$
\begin{aligned}
432 &= 400 + 30 + 2 = \overset{300}{\cancel{400}} + \overset{\overset{120}{\cancel{20}}}{\cancel{30}} + \overset{12}{\cancel{2}} \\
-\,273 &= \underline{200 + 70 + 3} = \underline{200 + 70 + 3}
\end{aligned}
$$

Paso 3 $\begin{cases} 100 + 50 + 9 \\ = 159 \end{cases}$

Paso 1 "Extender" cada número para mostrar que consta de centenas, decenas y unidades.

Paso 2 Observar si hay suficientes unidades para restar. Si no, desagrupar una decena para formar 10 unidades y sumarlas a las unidades existentes. Observar si hay suficientes decenas para restar. Si no, desagrupar una centena para formar 10 decenas y sumarlas a las decenas existentes. Los niños también pueden desagrupar por la izquierda.

Paso 3 Restar para hallar la respuesta. Los niños pueden restar de izquierda a derecha o de derecha a izquierda.

Método de desagrupar primero

Paso 1 Observar si hay suficientes unidades y decenas para restar. Desagrupar cuando haga falta.

Mirar dentro de 432. Desagrupar 432 y volver a nombrarlo como 3 centenas, 12 decenas y 12 unidades.

Desagrupar por la izquierda: **Desagrupar por la derecha:**

Paso 2 Restar para hallar la respuesta. Los niños pueden restar empezando por la izquierda o por la derecha.

Para explicar cualquier método que usen, los niños deben usar lenguaje y dibujos relacionados con centenas, decenas y unidades para demostrar que comprenden el valor posicional.

Si tiene alguna duda o comentario, por favor comuníquese conmigo.

Atentamente,
El maestro de su niño

Discuss Subtraction Problems

Solve each word problem. Use any method.
Make a proof drawing.

1 A teacher buys 200 erasers for his students. He gives 152 of them away. How many erasers does he have left over?

☐ _____
   label

2 The school cafeteria has 500 apples. Some of them are served with lunch. After lunch, there are 239 apples left. How many apples does the cafeteria serve?

☐ _____
   label

3 At the Music Megastore, there are 600 guitars for sale at the beginning of the month. At the end of the month, there are 359 guitars. How many guitars are sold?

☐ _____
   label

4 Jorge is on a basketball team. He scores 181 points one year. He scores some points in a second year, too. He scores a total of 400 points over the two years. How many points does he score the second year?

☐ _____
   label

Practice Subtracting from 1,000

Subtract. Use any method.

⑤
```
  1,0 0 0
 −  7 7 2
```

⑥
```
  1,0 0 0
 −  5 2 6
```

⑦
```
  1,0 0 0
 −  8 4 3
```

⑧
```
  1,0 0 0
 −  2 9 3
```

⑨
```
  1,0 0 0
 −    9 5
```

⑩
```
  1,0 0 0
 −  1 5 7
```

⑪ Elliot has 1,000 pennies. He puts 350 pennies in penny rolls. How many pennies are left?

label

⑫ Marta's class plans to collect 1,000 cans this year. They have 452 cans so far. How many more cans do they plan to collect?

label

 Check Understanding

Draw quick pictures to show how you solved Exercise 6.

Subtract from Hundreds Numbers

Name _____

Do I Need to Ungroup?

Decide if you need to ungroup. If you need to ungroup, draw a magnifying glass around the top number.
Then find the answer.

①
$$\begin{array}{r} 5\,0\,8 \\ -\,3\,4\,6 \\ \hline \end{array}$$

Ungroup to get 10 ones? _____

Ungroup to get 10 tens? _____

②
$$\begin{array}{r} 5\,0\,0 \\ -\,3\,0\,6 \\ \hline \end{array}$$

Ungroup to get 10 ones? _____

Ungroup to get 10 tens? _____

③
$$\begin{array}{r} 6\,7\,0 \\ -\,3\,4\,0 \\ \hline \end{array}$$

Ungroup to get 10 ones? _____

Ungroup to get 10 tens? _____

④
$$\begin{array}{r} 5\,7\,0 \\ -\,3\,9\,0 \\ \hline \end{array}$$

Ungroup to get 10 ones? _____

Ungroup to get 10 tens? _____

Subtract from Numbers with Zeros **357**

Subtract from 3-Digit Numbers with Zeros

Subtract.

⑤
```
   406
 - 181
```

⑥
```
   790
 - 272
```

⑦
```
   340
 - 118
```

⑧
```
   507
 - 438
```

⑨
```
   400
 - 263
```

⑩
```
   500
 - 234
```

PATH to FLUENCY Add and Subtract Within 100

Add.

⑪
```
   38
 + 44
```

⑫
```
   61
 + 17
```

⑬
```
   36
 + 64
```

⑭
```
   78
 + 19
```

Subtract.

⑮
```
   100
 -  57
```

⑯
```
   92
 - 40
```

⑰
```
   64
 - 25
```

⑱
```
   81
 - 19
```

 Check Understanding

Explain how you know when to ungroup in subtraction.

Subtract from Numbers with Zeros

Name _____

Practice and Represent 3-Digit Subtraction

Solve. Show your work.

1
```
  4 7 3
- 3 5 4
```

2
```
  8 2 8
- 3 8 1
```

3
```
  2 1 5
- 1 6 1
```

4
```
  5 2 6
- 2 5 9
```

5
```
  6 8 6
- 2 5 9
```

6
```
  9 1 7
- 2 6 1
```

Practice and Represent 3-Digit Subtraction (continued)

Solve. Show your work.

7
$$\begin{array}{r} 368 \\ -\ 179 \\ \hline \end{array}$$

8
$$\begin{array}{r} 999 \\ -\ 236 \\ \hline \end{array}$$

What's the Error?

$$\begin{array}{r} 903 \\ -\ 647 \\ \hline 344 \end{array}$$

Am I correct?

9 Show Puzzled Penguin how you would solve the problem.

$$\begin{array}{r} 9\ 0\ 3 \\ -\ 6\ 4\ 7 \\ \hline 2\ 5\ 6 \end{array}$$

 Check Understanding

Explain how to ungroup to solve 752 − 384.

    Subtract from Any 3-Digit Number

Practice with Ungrouping

Solve. Show your work.

1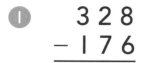
$$\begin{array}{r} 3\,2\,8 \\ -\,1\,7\,6 \\ \hline \end{array}$$

How many times
did you ungroup?

_____

2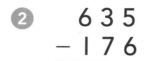
$$\begin{array}{r} 6\,3\,5 \\ -\,1\,7\,6 \\ \hline \end{array}$$

How many times
did you ungroup?

_____

3 $$\begin{array}{r} 4\,8\,0 \\ -\,1\,7\,6 \\ \hline \end{array}$$

How many times
did you ungroup?

_____

4 $$\begin{array}{r} 2\,9\,7 \\ -\,1\,7\,6 \\ \hline \end{array}$$

How many times
did you ungroup?

_____

Practice with Ungrouping (continued)

Solve. Show your work.

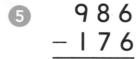
5
```
  986
− 176
```

How many times
did you ungroup?

_____

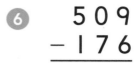
6
```
  509
− 176
```

How many times
did you ungroup?

_____

7
```
  800
− 176
```

How many times
did you ungroup?

_____

8
```
  570
− 176
```

How many times
did you ungroup?

_____

Practice Ungrouping

Name _____

Round to the Nearest Hundred

Round 268 to the nearest hundred. Follow these steps:

Step 1: Underline the number in the hundreds place.   **2**68

Step 2: Write the hundred that is greater than 268 above
and write the hundred that is less than 268 below.

Step 3: Make a drawing to show each number.

Step 4: If there are 5 or more <u>tens</u>, round up.
If there are fewer than 5 <u>tens</u>, round down.

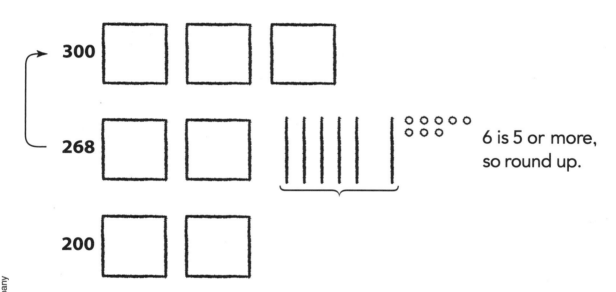

6 is 5 or more,
so round up.

Practice Rounding

Round the number to the nearest hundred. You may use drawings.

9 112 [   ]   **10** 283 [   ]

11 242 [   ]   **12** 439 [   ]

13 664 [   ]   **14** 553 [   ]

Round to Estimate Answers

Round each number to the nearest hundred.
Then add or subtract the rounded numbers.
Circle the answer that is the better estimate.

⑮
$$\begin{array}{r} 2\,1\,4 \\ +\,1\,2\,4 \\ \hline \end{array}$$

200　or　300

⑯
$$\begin{array}{r} 3\,8\,0 \\ +\,2\,3\,4 \\ \hline \end{array}$$

600　or　800

⑰
$$\begin{array}{r} 4\,6\,6 \\ +\,1\,7\,7 \\ \hline \end{array}$$

600　or　700

⑱
$$\begin{array}{r} 6\,2\,3 \\ -\,2\,2\,1 \\ \hline \end{array}$$

400　or　500

⑲
$$\begin{array}{r} 8\,6\,1 \\ -\,3\,7\,4 \\ \hline \end{array}$$

400　or　500

⑳
$$\begin{array}{r} 4\,8\,4 \\ -\,2\,3\,7 \\ \hline \end{array}$$

200　or　300

Solve by rounding.　　　　　　　　　　　　　　**Show your work.**

㉑ Warren scored 411 points in the first game
and 385 points in the second game. Round
each number to the nearest hundred. *About*
how many points did Warren score altogether?

about ☐ _____
　　　　　　　　label

✓ Check Understanding

Explain how to use rounding to estimate the
difference of 782 − 278.

Subtract.

①   5 0 8
    − 3 7 1
    ───────

②   4 0 0
    − 1 6 9
    ───────

Solve.   **Show your work.**

③ Mr. Decker bought 300 pencils.
He gave 183 of the pencils away.
How many pencils does he have left over?

[   ] _____
label

④ Gina wants to save 1,000 dimes.
She has saved 681 so far.
How many more dimes does she need to save?

[   ] _____
label

⑤ Rick has 742 stamps.
He gives 671 of them to Amy.
How many stamps does Rick have left?

[   ] _____
label

Name _____

Date _____

Add or subtract.

1. $15 - 2 = \boxed{}$

2. $19 - 6 = \boxed{}$

3. $16 - 10 = \boxed{}$

4. $12 + 7 = \boxed{}$

5. $9 + 5 = \boxed{}$

6. $13 + 7 = \boxed{}$

7.
$$\begin{array}{r} 38 \\ -\ 20 \\ \hline \end{array}$$

8.
$$\begin{array}{r} 47 \\ +\ 43 \\ \hline \end{array}$$

9.
$$\begin{array}{r} 27 \\ -\ 14 \\ \hline \end{array}$$

10.
$$\begin{array}{r} 61 \\ -\ 12 \\ \hline \end{array}$$

11.
$$\begin{array}{r} 35 \\ +\ 33 \\ \hline \end{array}$$

12.
$$\begin{array}{r} 71 \\ +\ 19 \\ \hline \end{array}$$

13.
$$\begin{array}{r} 67 \\ +\ 15 \\ \hline \end{array}$$

14.
$$\begin{array}{r} 29 \\ +\ 62 \\ \hline \end{array}$$

15.
$$\begin{array}{r} 69 \\ +\ 24 \\ \hline \end{array}$$

Review Addition and Subtraction

Loop *add* or *subtract*. Check if you need to ungroup or make a new ten or hundred. Then find the answer.

 1
$$\begin{array}{r} 7\,6\,2 \\ -\,3\,9\,5 \\ \hline \end{array}$$

subtract

☐ ungroup to get 10 ones

☐ ungroup to get 10 tens

add

☐ make 1 new ten

☐ make 1 new hundred

 2
$$\begin{array}{r} 3\,9\,5 \\ +\,3\,6\,7 \\ \hline \end{array}$$

subtract

☐ ungroup to get 10 ones

☐ ungroup to get 10 tens

add

☐ make 1 new ten

☐ make 1 new hundred

3
$$\begin{array}{r} 2\,8\,7 \\ -\,1\,9\,3 \\ \hline \end{array}$$

subtract

☐ ungroup to get 10 ones

☐ ungroup to get 10 tens

add

☐ make 1 new ten

☐ make 1 new hundred

4
$$\begin{array}{r} 4\,3\,7 \\ +\,3\,2\,4 \\ \hline \end{array}$$

subtract

☐ ungroup to get 10 ones

☐ ungroup to get 10 tens

add

☐ make 1 new ten

☐ make 1 new hundred

Relate Addition and Subtraction

VOCABULARY
opposite operation

Decide whether you need to add or subtract.
Draw a Math Mountain. Check your answer by using
the **opposite operation**.

⑤   532
   − 1 8 1   ✓

⑥   532
   + 1 8 1   ✓

⑦   528
   + 3 5 7   ✓

⑧   1,000
   − 4 3 8   ✓

⑨   571
   + 2 8 7   ✓

⑩   904
   − 4 5 8   ✓

Check Understanding

Draw a Math Mountain to show the solution
for 847 − 266.

Solve and Discuss

Make a drawing. Write an equation.
Solve the problem.

1 Lucero spills a bag of marbles. 219 fall on the floor. 316 are still in the bag. How many were in the bag in the beginning?

_____
label

2 Al counts bugs in the park. He counts 561 in March. He counts 273 fewer than that in April. How many bugs does he count in April?

_____
label

3 Happy the Clown gives out balloons. She gives out 285 at the zoo and then gives out some more at the amusement park. Altogether she gives out 503 balloons. How many balloons does she give out at the amusement park?

_____
label

4 Charlie the Clown gives out 842 balloons at the fun fair. He gives out 194 at the store. He gives out 367 at the playground. How many more balloons does he give out at the fun fair than at the playground?

_____
label

Mixed Addition and Subtraction Word Problems **369**

Solve and Discuss (continued)

Make a drawing. Write an equation.
Solve the problem.

5 Damon collects stamps. He has 383 stamps. Then he buys 126 more at a yard sale. How many stamps does he have now?

label

6 Mr. Lewis sells 438 melons. Now he has 294 melons left. How many melons did he have at the start?

label

7 Ali is giving out ribbons for a race. She gave out 57 ribbons so far, and she has 349 ribbons left. How many ribbons did she have at the start?

label

8 Cora collected 542 sports cards last year. She collected 247 fewer than that this year. How many cards did she collect in both years together?

label

Mixed Addition and Subtraction Word Problems

Name _____

Solve and Discuss (continued)

Make a drawing. Write an equation. Solve the problem.

9 Ms. Andy is working on a puzzle. She has placed 643 pieces. There are 1,000 pieces in the puzzle. How many more pieces does she have to place?

[   ] _____
label

10 In March the Shaws plant some flowers. In April they plant 178 more flowers. In the two months they plant a total of 510 flowers. How many flowers do they plant in March?

[   ] _____
label

11 Jeremy has 48 action figures. Jeremy has 14 more action figures than Keith. How many action figures does Keith have?

[   ] _____
label

12 Mr. Pawel gives out flyers about a play. He gives out 194 flyers at the bakery. He gives out 358 flyers at the grocery store. How many fewer flyers does he give out at the bakery than at the grocery store?

[   ] _____
label

Mixed Addition and Subtraction Word Problems **371**

Solve and Discuss (continued)

Make a drawing. Write an equation. Solve the problem.

13 There are 675 plastic cups and 300 paper plates in a cabinet. Jaime puts more cups and plates in the cabinet. Now there are 850 cups. How many cups does Jaime add?

	_____
	label

14 Last week Miss Bee sold some tickets to a play. She sells 345 more this week. Altogether she sells 500 tickets. How many tickets did she sell last week?

	_____
	label

15 April has 98 fewer pennies than Julie has. April has 521 pennies. How many pennies does Julie have?

	_____
	label

 Check Understanding

Complete the comparison bars for this problem:

Ms. Vaughn has 342 buttons. She has 163 more buttons than Mr. Wheel. How many buttons does Mr. Wheel have?

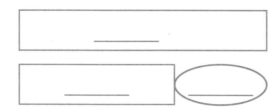

Mixed Addition and Subtraction Word Problems

Name _____

Solve Problems at the Art Fair

Many artists sell their work at art fairs.

Solve.

1. On one weekend, 489 people come to the art fair on Saturday and 511 people come to the fair on Sunday. How many people come to the fair in all?

☐ _____
        label

2. Wendy uses silver and blue beads to make necklaces to sell. She uses 72 blue beads. She uses 38 more blue beads than silver beads. How many silver beads does she use?

☐ _____
        label

3. LeBron uses tiny seed beads to make bracelets. He buys a package of seed beads with 350 red beads and 250 white beads. After he makes the bracelets for the fair, he has just 6 beads left. How many beads does he use?

☐ _____
        label

Caricatures

A caricature is a drawing of a person.
The drawing looks like a cartoon.

- Last week, an artist drew
  146 children and 84 adults.

- This week, the artist drew
  167 children and 55 adults.

Solve. Use the information in the box above.

4 How many people did the artist draw last week?

_____
label

5 How many people did the artist draw this week?

_____
label

6 How many fewer people did the artist draw
this week than last week?

_____
label

7 Did the artist draw more children or more adults?

more _____

Add. Subtract to check.

1.
```
    4 3 1
  + 2 7 2
  _____
```

Subtract. Add to check.

2.
```
    5 4 3
  - 1 9 2
  _____
```

Solve.   **Show your work.**

3. Jim grows 398 pounds of corn. Roberto grows 475 pounds of corn. How many more pounds of corn does Roberto grow than Jim?

```
┌──────┐
│      │  _____
└──────┘        label
```

4. Joe loads 268 bales of hay onto the truck. 317 bales of hay still need to be loaded. How many bales of hay are there altogether?

```
┌──────┐
│      │  _____
└──────┘        label
```

5. Lindsey lives 593 miles from May's house and 417 miles from Chad's house. How many more miles does she live from May's house than Chad's house?

```
┌──────┐
│      │  _____
└──────┘        label
```

Name _____ **Date** _____

PATH to FLUENCY

Add or subtract.

1 $13 + 5 =$ ☐   **2** $19 + 1 =$ ☐   **3** $11 + 2 =$ ☐

4 $15 - 7 =$ ☐   **5** $16 - 9 =$ ☐   **6** $14 - 12 =$ ☐

7
$$\begin{array}{r} 36 \\ -26 \\ \hline \end{array}$$

8
$$\begin{array}{r} 77 \\ -58 \\ \hline \end{array}$$

9
$$\begin{array}{r} 31 \\ +13 \\ \hline \end{array}$$

10
$$\begin{array}{r} 65 \\ +16 \\ \hline \end{array}$$

11
$$\begin{array}{r} 24 \\ + 6 \\ \hline \end{array}$$

12
$$\begin{array}{r} 39 \\ +45 \\ \hline \end{array}$$

13
$$\begin{array}{r} 87 \\ -19 \\ \hline \end{array}$$

14
$$\begin{array}{r} 100 \\ - 64 \\ \hline \end{array}$$

15
$$\begin{array}{r} 70 \\ -38 \\ \hline \end{array}$$

1 Write the number that is shown by the drawing.

| | | | | | ° ° °

_____   _____   _____   Total _____
Hundreds   Tens   Ones

---

2 Ming has some baseball cards. He gives 210 of them away. Now he has 323 cards. How many baseball cards did Ming have to start? Circle the number to complete the sentence.

Ming had
| 113 |
| 503 |
| 533 |
cards to start.

---

3 Is this a way to show 613? Choose Yes or No.

6 + 1 + 3   ○ Yes   ○ No

600 + 10 + 3   ○ Yes   ○ No

six hundred thirty-one   ○ Yes   ○ No

six hundred thirteen   ○ Yes   ○ No

---

4 Robin had 630 coins in her collection. She gave 198 coins to her brother. Round each number to the nearest hundred. *About* how many coins does Robin have now?

Show your work.

about [ ] _____
                label

5 Choose the ways that show counting by 10s.

○ 430   431   432   433   434   435   436   437
○ 260   270   280   290   300   310   320   330
○ 200   300   400   500   600   700   800   900
○ 510   520   530   540   550   560   570   580
○ 930   940   950   960   970   980   990   1,000

6 Count by 100s. Write the numbers.

300   400 _____   _____   _____   _____   _____   _____

7 The Nature Club made a 4-page flyer of nature photos.
They want to print 100 copies of the flyer. They have
258 sheets of paper. They buy a pack of 200 sheets.
Do they have enough paper to print the flyers? Explain.

_____

_____

_____

The club adds one more page of photos to each flyer.
Do they have enough paper to print them now? Explain.

_____

_____

_____

8 Match the numbers to <, =, or >.

461 ◯ 416 •   • =

324 ◯ 324 •   • <

692 ◯ 902 •   • >

---

9 On Tuesday, 222 books are returned to the library. 387 books are returned on Wednesday. Round each number to the nearest hundred. *About* how many books are returned to the library?

about ☐ _____
           label

---

10 Add. Then choose Yes or No about what you did.

```
  5 7 4
+ 3 2 6
```

Did you make a new ten?   ○ Yes   ○ No

Did you make a new hundred?   ○ Yes   ○ No

Did you make a new thousand? ○ Yes   ○ No

---

11 Samira has 285 beads. 96 of them are red. The rest of the beads are blue. How many blue beads does Samira have?

Show your work.

☐ _____
     label

Solve.

12 $596 - 100 =$ _____

13 $603 - 10 =$ _____

---

14 Ada read 124 pages in a book. The book has
300 pages. How many more pages does she
still have to read to finish the book?

Make a drawing. Write an equation.
Solve the problem.

[   ] _____

           label

---

15 Show and explain how to subtract 279 from 458.
Use the words *hundreds*, *tens*, and *ones*. Explain
how and why you can use addition to check your answer.

_____

_____

_____

_____

_____

_____

Boxes of Marbles

Solve and check. Use place value.
Show your work.

Celia and Anthony collect marbles.

┌─────────────────────────┐
│   Celia's Marbles   │
│   167   │
└─────────────────────────┘

┌─────────────────────────┐
│   Anthony's Marbles   │
│   176   │
└─────────────────────────┘

1 Do Celia and Anthony have the same number
of marbles? How do you know?

_____

_____

_____

2 To play a game, Celia and Anthony must first put their
marbles into bags of 10.

How many bags of 10 marbles can Celia fill? ☐

How many bags of 10 marbles can Anthony fill? ☐

If they put their marbles together first, can they fill
the same total number of bags? Explain.

_____

_____

_____

_____

3 Celia buys 16 new marbles. How many marbles does she have now? How does Celia's new number of marbles compare with the number of marbles Anthony has?

_____

_____

_____

4 Anthony wants to have 200 marbles in all. How many more marbles does he need? Tell how you solved the problem.

_____

_____

_____

_____

5 Explain how you could use addition or subtraction to check your answers in Problems 3 and 4.

_____

_____

_____

_____

Dear Family:

In this unit, your child will learn about rectangular arrays and how to use addition to count the number of objects in an array. The array below has 2 rows and 3 columns. It can be described as 2 rows with 3 tiles in each row, or 3 columns with 2 tiles in each column.

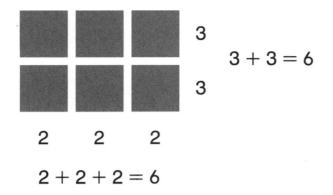

$$3 + 3 = 6$$

$$2 + 2 + 2 = 6$$

You can help your child by working with him or her to practice using the words *array*, *rows*, and *columns*. For example, ask your child to use pennies or other small objects to make an array that has 4 rows with 5 objects in each row. Ask your child to write the addition equations that show the total number of objects in the array. ($5 + 5 + 5 + 5 = 20$ and $4 + 4 + 4 + 4 + 4 = 20$)

Your child will also be learning about equal parts of circles and rectangles: 2 *halves*, 3 *thirds*, and 4 *fourths*. You can practice using this vocabulary at home. For example, "I am cutting this pizza into 4 fourths."

Please contact me if you have any questions or concerns.

Sincerely,
Your child's teacher

Estimada familia:

En esta unidad, su niño aprenderá acerca de las matrices rectangulares y aprenderá cómo usar la suma para contar el número de objetos en una matriz. La matriz de abajo tiene 2 hileras y 3 columnas. Puede describirse así: 2 hileras con 3 fichas en cada columna, o 3 columnas con 2 fichas en cada columna.

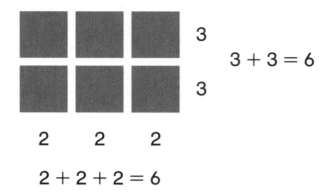

$$3 + 3 = 6$$

$$2 + 2 + 2 = 6$$

Usted puede ayudar a su niño practicando el uso de las palabras *matriz, hileras* y *columnas*. Por ejemplo, pídale que use monedas de un centavo u otros objetos pequeños para hacer una matriz que tenga 4 hileras con 5 objetos en cada una. Pida a su niño que escriba la ecuación de suma que muestra el número total de objetos en la matriz.
$(5 + 5 + 5 + 5 = 20$ y $4 + 4 + 4 + 4 + 4 = 20)$

Su niño también aprenderá acerca de partes iguales de círculos y rectángulos: 2 *medios,* 3 *tercios* y 4 *cuartos.* Pueden practicar usando este vocabulario en casa. Por ejemplo: "Estoy cortando esta pizza en 4 cuartos."

Si tiene alguna duda o algún comentario, por favor comuníquese conmigo.

Atentamente,
El maestro de su niño

array

fourths

columns

halves

equal shares

rows

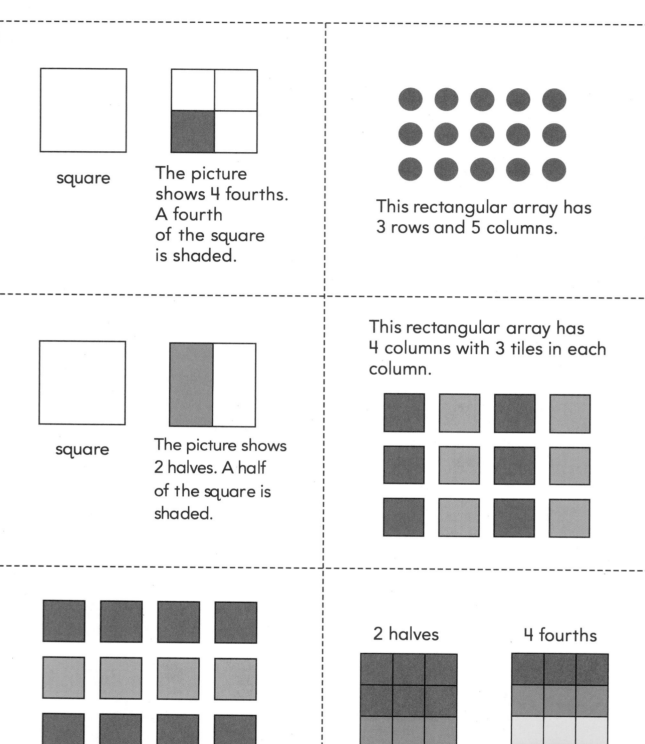

square

The picture
shows 4 fourths.
A fourth
of the square
is shaded.

This rectangular array has
3 rows and 5 columns.

square

The picture shows
2 halves. A half
of the square is
shaded.

This rectangular array has
4 columns with 3 tiles in each
column.

This rectangular array has
3 rows with 4 tiles in each row.

2 halves   4 fourths

thirds

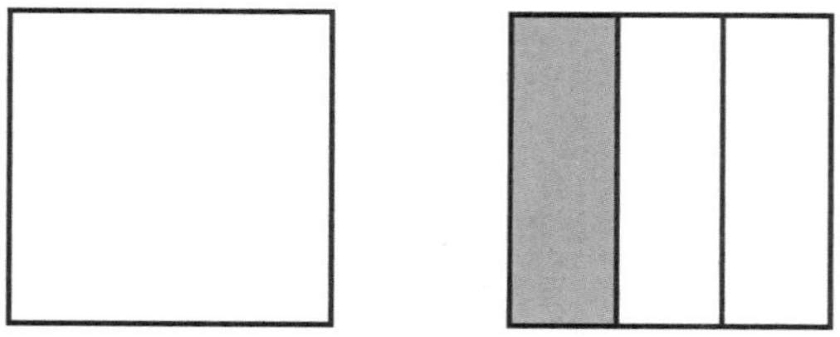

square

The picture shows 3 thirds. A third of the square is shaded.

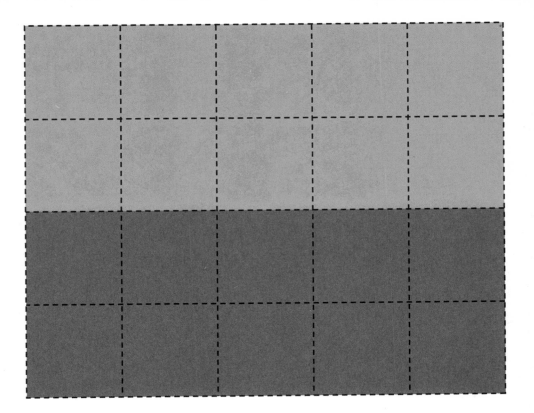

Square-Inch Tiles **385**

Square-Inch Tiles

Rows and Columns

1 Circle the **rows**.

2 Circle the **columns**.

Use Arrays

3 Write how many pears in each row and in each column.

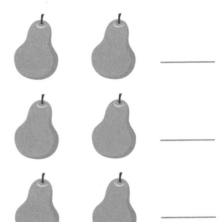

_____

_____

_____

_____   _____

4 Write two equations for the **array**.

_____

_____

5 Skip count by 2s to find the total number of pears.

_____, _____, _____

6 Skip count by 3s to find the total number of pears.

_____, _____

7 How many pears are there?

_____ pears

Use Arrays (continued)

8 Write how many stars in each row and in each column.

_____   _____   _____   _____

9 Write two equations for the array.

_____

_____

10 Skip count by 4s to find the total number of stars.

_____ , _____

11 Skip count by 2s to find the total number of stars.

_____ , _____ , _____ , _____

12 How many stars are there?

_____ stars

13 How many stars would there be if the array had one less row?

_____ stars

14 How many stars would there be if the array had one less column?

_____ stars

Arrays, Partitioned Rectangles, and Equal Shares

Name _____

Use Patterns to Solve Problems

Sam collects two shells each day. He collects shells for six days. How many shells does Sam collect?

shell

15 Draw an array to solve this problem.

Sam collects _____ shells.

16 What counting pattern could you use to find the number of shells?

_____

17 Skip count to find the number of shells.

_____

18 Draw an array to match this pattern:
3, 6, 9, 12

19 What counting pattern does this show?

_____

20 Write the next two numbers in the pattern.

_____

Arrays, Partitioned Rectangles, and Equal Shares **389**

Measure to Partition Rectangles

Measure in inches. Draw rows and columns.
Write the number of small squares.

㉑ _____ squares

㉒ _____ squares

Measure in centimeters. Draw rows and columns.
Write the number of small squares.

㉓ _____ squares

㉔ _____ squares

㉕ _____ squares

Arrays, Partitioned Rectangles, and Equal Shares

Name _____

Shade Equal Shares

Measure in centimeters. Draw rows and columns.
Shade to show **halves**, **thirds**, and **fourths**.

26 halves

27 thirds

28 fourths

Measure in centimeters. Draw rows and columns.

29 Shade to show halves two different ways.

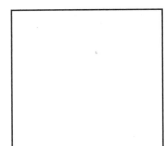

30 Shade to show fourths two different ways.

31 Shade to show halves two different ways.

Arrays, Partitioned Rectangles, and Equal Shares **391**

More Practice with Equal Shares and Partitions

VOCABULARY
equal shares

Shade to show **equal shares**.

32 2 halves

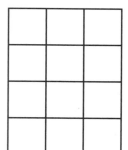

33 3 thirds

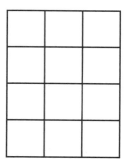

34 4 fourths

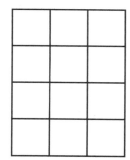

Measure in centimeters. Draw rows and columns. Write the number of small squares.

35

_____ squares

36

_____ squares

37

_____ squares

38

_____ squares

✓ **Check Understanding**

Explain one way to use addition to find the number of small squares in the array for Exercise 38.

Arrays, Partitioned Rectangles, and Equal Shares

Circles and Rectangles **393**

Circles and Rectangles

Name _____

Different Shapes of a Half of the Same Rectangle

1 Make two halves. Show different ways. Shade half of each rectangle.

Different Shapes of a Third of the Same Rectangle

2 Make three thirds. Show different ways. Shade a third of each rectangle.

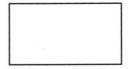 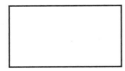

Different Shapes of a Fourth of the Same Rectangle

3 Make four fourths. Show different ways. Shade a fourth of each rectangle.

 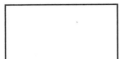  

Equal Shares Using the Same Square

4 Make 2 equal shares. Show different ways. Shade half of each square.

5 Make 3 equal shares. Show different ways. Shade a third of each square.

6 Make 4 equal shares. Show different ways. Shade a fourth of each square.

Equal Shares Using the Same Circle

7 Make 2 equal shares. Shade half of the circle.

8 Make 3 equal shares. Shade a third of the circle.

9 Make 4 equal shares. Shade a fourth of the circle.

Different Shape but Same Size

10 Use Drawings 1, 2, and 3 to explain why the blue and yellow shares are equal.

 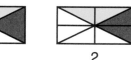

1   2   3

 Check Understanding

Fill in the blanks to correctly complete the statement.

I know equal shares are the same shape if I can place

one share exactly on _____ of another share.

I might have to rotate or _____ the share.

Find Equal Shares

Write how many in each row and in each column.
Then write two addition equations for the array.

1

_____ _____ _____ _____ _____

_____

_____

Measure in centimeters. Draw rows and columns.
Write the number of small squares.

2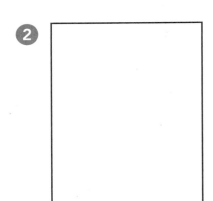

_____ squares

3

_____ squares

Make two halves. Show different ways.

4

Shade half of the circle.

5

Name _____ **Date** _____

PATH to
FLUENCY

Add or subtract.

1 $7 + 7 = \boxed{}$ 2 $8 + 9 = \boxed{}$ 3 $12 + 6 = \boxed{}$

4 $11 - 8 = \boxed{}$ 5 $16 - 8 = \boxed{}$ 6 $13 - 7 = \boxed{}$

7
$$\begin{array}{r} 45 \\ +\,47 \\ \hline \end{array}$$

8
$$\begin{array}{r} 21 \\ +\,35 \\ \hline \end{array}$$

9
$$\begin{array}{r} 53 \\ +\,28 \\ \hline \end{array}$$

10
$$\begin{array}{r} 42 \\ -\,31 \\ \hline \end{array}$$

11
$$\begin{array}{r} 72 \\ -\,34 \\ \hline \end{array}$$

12
$$\begin{array}{r} 57 \\ -\,18 \\ \hline \end{array}$$

13
$$\begin{array}{r} 87 \\ -\,78 \\ \hline \end{array}$$

14
$$\begin{array}{r} 91 \\ -\,72 \\ \hline \end{array}$$

15
$$\begin{array}{r} 100 \\ -\,43 \\ \hline \end{array}$$

Solve and Discuss

Solve.   **Show your work.**

① Carl draws a line segment that is 18 centimeters long.
Then he makes it 14 centimeters longer. How long
is the line segment now?

☐ _____
              unit

② Samantha runs 45 meters, stops, then runs some more.
She runs a total of 95 meters. How many meters does
she run after her stop?

☐ _____
              unit

③ A ribbon is 48 inches long. Taylor uses 32 inches of the
ribbon to make a bow. How much ribbon is left?

☐ _____
              unit

④ Mr. Parker cut 9 feet from the end of a pole. The pole
is now 22 feet long. How long was the pole before
Mr. Parker cut it?

☐ _____
              unit

Solve and Discuss (continued)

Solve.   **Show your work.**

5 A race course is 99 meters long. There are trees along 38 meters of the course. How long is the part of the course without trees?

☐ _____
              unit

6 Ms. Godwin paints a fence that is 81 feet long. Mr. Sendak paints a fence that is 56 feet long. How much longer is the fence Ms. Godwin paints?

☐ _____
              unit

7 O'Shanti has a necklace that is 24 centimeters long. She makes the necklace 36 centimeters longer. How long is the necklace now?

☐ _____
              unit

8 A giant flag is 6 meters long. Vern adds 4 meters to its length. How long is the flag now?

☐ _____
              unit

Name _____

Solve and Discuss (continued)

Solve.   **Show your work.**

---

9 Kelly has a piece of red yarn that is 25 centimeters long. She also has a piece of blue yarn that is 11 centimeters long. How much longer is the red yarn than the blue yarn?

☐ _____
            unit

---

10 Paco swims 41 meters. Kenny swims 4 meters less than Paco. How far does Kenny swim?

☐ _____
            unit

---

11 Leonard walks 28 meters. Then he walks 56 more meters. How many meters does he walk in all?

☐ _____
            unit

---

12 A tree is 72 inches tall now. It is 12 inches taller than it was last year. How tall was the tree last year?

☐ _____
            unit

Number Line Diagrams

Use the number line diagram to add or subtract.

13 Loop 17 and 28. Loop the difference *D*.

How long is it? _____

14 Loop 17 and 35. Loop the difference *D*.

How long is it? _____

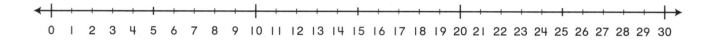

15 Loop 38 and 84. Loop the difference *D*.

How long is it? _____

16 Loop 67. Add 26 to it. Loop the total *T*.

How long is it? _____

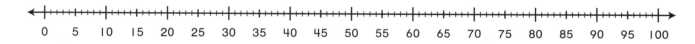
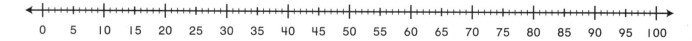

✓ **Check Understanding**

Explain how solving a length word problem is different from solving other word problems.

Length Word Problems and Number Line Diagrams

Name _____

Lengths at the Grocery Store

Choose a method to solve the problems. Does your method work for all of the problems? Be ready to explain your method to the class.

---

1 Someone spills a carton of juice in the store. Mr. Green cleans it up. Then he blocks off the wet spot with tape. How long is the tape?

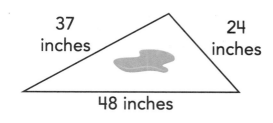

37 inches   24 inches

48 inches

[   ] _____
            unit

---

2 Mrs. Chang wants to decorate the table she uses for free food samples. She wants to put gold trim around the top of the table. How much trim will she need?

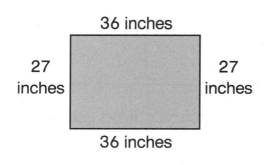

36 inches

27 inches   27 inches

36 inches

[   ] _____
            unit

---

3 Here is the route a customer takes while shopping at the store. How far does the customer walk altogether?

[   ] _____
            unit

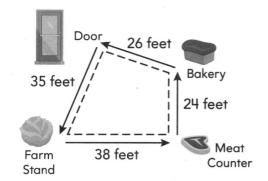

Door   26 feet
                    Bakery
35 feet
                    24 feet
Farm   38 feet   Meat
Stand   Counter

Playground Lengths

Solve.   **Show your work.**

4 The basketball court has four right angles and sides that are 42 feet, 37 feet, 42 feet, and 37 feet. What is the distance around the court?

[ ] _____
        unit

5 The fence around the picnic area has sides with lengths of 33 yards, 56 yards, and 61 yards. What is the total length of the fence?

[ ] _____
        unit

6 A playground game is outlined in chalk. Each of the four sides is 48 inches long and there are four right angles. What is the total length of the outline?

[ ] _____
        unit

7 The play area has a wood border. The border has sides that are 32 feet, 45 feet, 29 feet, and 61 feet. What is distance around the play area?

[ ] _____
        unit

Add Three and Four Lengths

Name _____

Distance Around Shapes at Home

Solve.   **Show your work.**

---

8 A border outlines a flower bed.
How long is the border?

55 inches

29 inches   32 inches

60 inches

[ ] _____
          unit

---

9 The pantry has a tiled floor.
What is the distance around
the tiled floor?

49 inches

24 inches   24 inches

49 inches

[ ] _____
          unit

---

10 In spring, all of the wood floors
get waxed. This part of the
library floor was waxed. What
is the distance around the
waxed part?

13 feet   12 feet

21 feet

[ ] _____
          unit

Distance Around Shapes at School

Solve.   **Show your work.**

---

11 A picture hanging in the library has sides that are 39 inches, 28 inches, 39 inches, and 28 inches. What is the distance around the picture?

_____
unit

12 The second grade class makes an art project. The lengths of the sides of the project are 18 inches, 24 inches, and 19 inches. The teacher wants to frame the project with tape. How much tape does she need?

_____
unit

---

13 The cafeteria is a square room. Each side measures 47 feet. What is the distance around the room?

_____
unit

14 The school patio has 4 sides. The lengths of the sides are 22 feet, 18 feet, 27 feet, and 16 feet. What is the distance around the patio?

_____
unit

 Check Understanding

Draw to show the method you used to add the three numbers in Problem 12.

Add Three and Four Lengths

Solve and Discuss

Solve.   **Show your work.**

① Miss Springfield is building shelves. The bottom shelf is 64 inches long. The top shelf is 27 inches longer than the bottom shelf. How long is the top shelf?

_____

② The top of a bookcase is 24 inches from the ceiling. The ceiling is 96 inches tall. How tall is the bookcase?

_____

③ Mr. Tracy is putting a border of rocks around his garden. The lengths of the sides of the garden are 12 feet, 19 feet, and 27 feet. How long will the border be?

_____

④ Brendan is knitting a scarf. It is 28 centimeters long. Then he knits 18 centimeters more. How long is the scarf now?

_____

Length Word Problems

Solve.   **Show your work.**

⑤ Hannah has a red ribbon and a blue ribbon.
The red ribbon is 17 cm long. The blue ribbon is 13 cm long.
How much longer is the red ribbon than the blue ribbon?

_____

⑥ A roll of tape is 76 feet long to start.
Mr. Novak uses 24 feet of the tape.
How much tape is left?

_____

⑦ Nick and Ben are running a relay race.
Nick runs 48 meters. Ben runs 37 meters.
How many fewer meters does Ben run?

_____

⑧ Mrs. Rossi is putting a fence around her garden.
The garden has 4 sides and 4 right angles.
Each side of the garden is 23 feet long.
How long will the fence be?

_____

More Length Word Problems

Name _____

Length Word Problems (continued)

Solve.   **Show your work.**

9 Caroline uses tape to mark off the space where
new grass was planted. The lengths of the sides of
the space are 16 feet, 28 feet, 36 feet, and 18 feet.
How much tape is needed?

_____

10 Mr. Morris pulls the shade down.
It covers 24 inches of the window.
Mrs. Morris pulls it down 48 more inches.
How much of the window is covered now?

_____

11 A flagpole is 62 feet tall.
The flag covers 11 feet of the pole.
How long is the part of the pole
that is not covered by the flag?

_____

12 Miguel is putting a string of lights around a sign.
The lengths of the sides of the sign are
26 inches, 18 inches, 26 inches, and 18 inches.
What length of lights does he need?

_____

What's the Error?

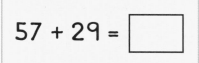

57 + 29 = ☐

I'm trying to add 57 and 29. I'm not sure what to do next.

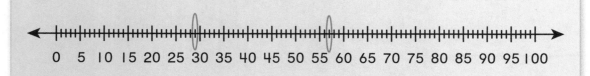

0 5 10 15 20 25 30 35 40 45 50 55 60 65 70 75 80 85 90 95 100

13 Show the equation on the number line diagram.
Use *T* for the total. Then find the unknown number.

$57 + 29 = $ ☐

← |‖‖|‖‖|‖‖|‖‖|‖‖|‖‖|‖‖|‖‖|‖‖|‖‖|‖‖|‖‖|‖‖|‖‖|‖‖|‖‖|‖‖|‖‖|‖‖|‖‖| →
0 5 10 15 20 25 30 35 40 45 50 55 60 65 70 75 80 85 90 95 100

Number Line Diagrams

Show the equation on the number line diagram.
Use *D* for the difference. Then find the unknown number.

14 ☐ $ + 28 = 86$

← |‖‖|‖‖|‖‖|‖‖|‖‖|‖‖|‖‖|‖‖|‖‖|‖‖|‖‖|‖‖|‖‖|‖‖|‖‖|‖‖|‖‖|‖‖|‖‖|‖‖| →
0 5 10 15 20 25 30 35 40 45 50 55 60 65 70 75 80 85 90 95 100

✓ **Check Understanding**

Look at the diagram. Complete the equation.

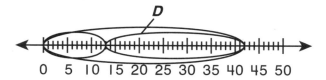

0 5 10 15 20 25 30 35 40 45 50

$13 + $ ☐ $ = 42$

More Length Word Problems

Name _____

Flags with Equal Parts

Ships can use flags to send messages. A flag can be used alone to send a message. A group of flags can be used to spell out a message.

This flag means "I have a pilot on board." It can also be used for the letter H.

1 How many parts does the flag have?

_____ parts

2 Does the flag show equal parts?

     yes   no

This flag means "Return to ship." It can also be used for the letter P.

3 How many parts does the flag have?

_____ parts

4 Does the flag show equal parts?

     yes   no

Square Flags

5 Draw a square flag. Show halves. Color the flag. Color a half of the flag blue.

6 Draw a square flag. Show thirds. Color the flag. Color a third of the flag red.

Rectangular Flags

7 Show 4 equal shares that are rectangles.

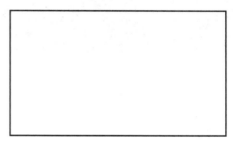

8 Show 4 equal shares that are triangles.

9 On a separate sheet of paper, design your own flag. Use equal parts. Color your flag.

Focus on Problem Solving

Name _____   Date _____

Show the equation on the number line diagram.
Use *T* for the total or *D* for the difference.
Then find the unknown number.

1 $48 + 31 =$ ☐

←|┼┼┼|┼┼┼|┼┼┼|┼┼┼|┼┼┼|┼┼┼|┼┼┼|┼┼┼|┼┼┼|┼┼┼|┼┼┼|┼┼┼|┼┼┼|┼┼┼|┼┼┼|┼┼┼|┼┼┼|┼┼┼|┼┼┼|┼┼┼|→
　0　5　10 15 20 25 30 35 40 45 50 55 60 65 70 75 80 85 90 95 100

2 $44 +$ ☐ $= 62$

←|┼┼┼|┼┼┼|┼┼┼|┼┼┼|┼┼┼|┼┼┼|┼┼┼|┼┼┼|┼┼┼|┼┼┼|┼┼┼|┼┼┼|┼┼┼|┼┼┼|┼┼┼|┼┼┼|┼┼┼|┼┼┼|┼┼┼|┼┼┼|→
　0　5　10 15 20 25 30 35 40 45 50 55 60 65 70 75 80 85 90 95 100

Solve.　　　　　　　　　　　　　　　　　　　　　　**Show your work.**

3 Marissa wants to decorate a table for a party.
She wants to put silver trim around the top
of the table. How much trim will she need?

42 inches

25 inches　　　　25 inches

42 inches

☐ _____
　　　　unit

4 A ribbon is 54 inches long. Grace uses
41 inches of the ribbon to make a gift.
How much ribbon is left?

☐ _____
　　　　unit

5 The red rope is 64 feet long. The yellow rope is
39 feet. How many feet shorter is the yellow rope?

☐ _____
　　　　unit

Name _____ **Date** _____

PATH to FLUENCY

Add or subtract.

1. $15 - 4 = \boxed{}$ 2. $15 - 12 = \boxed{}$ 3. $18 - 10 = \boxed{}$

4. $9 + 8 = \boxed{}$ 5. $12 + 6 = \boxed{}$ 6. $13 + 7 = \boxed{}$

7.
$$\begin{array}{r} 34 \\ -3 \\ \hline \end{array}$$

8.
$$\begin{array}{r} 45 \\ -19 \\ \hline \end{array}$$

9.
$$\begin{array}{r} 64 \\ -29 \\ \hline \end{array}$$

10.
$$\begin{array}{r} 28 \\ +41 \\ \hline \end{array}$$

11.
$$\begin{array}{r} 36 \\ +46 \\ \hline \end{array}$$

12.
$$\begin{array}{r} 58 \\ +14 \\ \hline \end{array}$$

13.
$$\begin{array}{r} 90 \\ -12 \\ \hline \end{array}$$

14.
$$\begin{array}{r} 95 \\ -69 \\ \hline \end{array}$$

15.
$$\begin{array}{r} 94 \\ -67 \\ \hline \end{array}$$

Name _____ Date _____

1 Write how many in each row and in each column.

 _____
_____
_____
_____

_____ _____ _____

2 Does the equation match the array above?
Choose Yes or No.

$3 + 3 + 3 = 9$ ○ Yes   ○ No

$4 + 4 + 4 = 12$ ○ Yes   ○ No

$3 + 3 + 3 + 3 = 12$ ○ Yes   ○ No

$4 + 4 + 4 + 4 = 16$ ○ Yes   ○ No

3 Measure in centimeters.
Draw rows and columns. Write
the number of small squares.

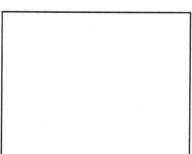

_____ squares

4 Measure in inches.
Draw rows and columns. Write
the number of small squares.

_____ squares

5 Look at these shapes.

Are the shaded parts the same shape? Explain.

_____

Are the shaded parts the same size? Explain.

_____

_____

6 Draw lines in each shape to make equal shares.

Two Halves	Three Thirds	Four Fourths
◯	◯	◯
▭	▭	▭

7 Choose the squares that show a third shaded.

◯   ◯   ◯   ◯   ◯

Solve. Circle the number to complete the sentence.

8 Jennifer has 66 inches of red yarn.
She has 14 more inches of blue yarn than red yarn.
How many inches of blue yarn does Jennifer have?

Jennifer has | 70
80 | inches of blue yarn.
90

9 Elizabeth is shoveling snow from
a sidewalk that is 20 feet long.
So far she has shoveled 6 feet of the sidewalk.
How many more feet does she need to shovel?

Elizabeth needs to shovel | 14
16 | more feet.
26

Write an equation and solve.

10 Jake is using fencing to make a dog pen. The pen has
three sides. Two sides are 6 feet long. The third side is
3 feet long. How many feet of fencing does Jake need?

11 Devon uses gold ribbon to make a border
around a square picture. Each side of the
picture is 14 centimeters long. How many
centimeters of gold ribbon does Devon need?

12 Write a term from a tile to tell
how much is shaded.

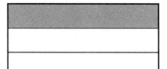

_____   _____   _____

---

13 Complete the equation that the number line
diagram represents.

0   5   10   15   20   25   30   35   40   45   50   55   60   65   70   75   80   85   90   95   100

$\boxed{} + 15 = \boxed{}$

---

14 Show the equation on the number line diagram.
Use *T* for the total.
Then find the unknown number.

$46 + 21 = \boxed{}$

0   5   10   15   20   25   30   35   40   45   50   55   60   65   70   75   80   85   90   95   100

Marching Band

1 The 8 drummers in a marching band line up in equal rows. Show one way they could line up. Shade a ☐ to show each drummer.

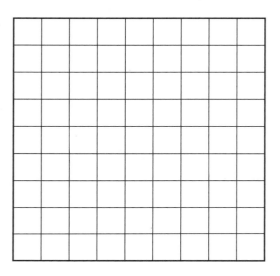

2 Show a different way the 8 drummers could line up in equal rows.

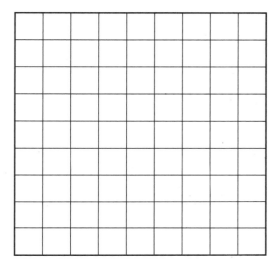

3 Write an addition equation for each array.

_____

_____

4 Half of the drummers go home. Can the remaining drummers still line up in equal rows? Explain your thinking.

_____

_____

There are 60 students in the marching band.
There are 8 band members who are drummers
and 5 band members who play the flute.
How many band members do not play the drum or flute?

5 Explain how you would solve the problem.

_____

_____

_____

_____

_____

6 Write an addition equation to solve the problem.
Use ■ to represent the unknown number.
Circle the total in the equation.
Underline the unknown addend.

_____

7 Show the equation on the number line diagram.
Use *D* for the difference.
Then write the answer.

←|┼┼┼|┼┼┼|┼┼┼|┼┼┼|┼┼┼|┼┼┼|┼┼┼|┼┼┼|┼┼┼|┼┼┼|┼┼┼|┼┼┼|┼┼┼|┼┼┼|┼┼┼|┼┼┼|┼┼┼|┼┼┼|┼┼┼|┼┼┼|→

0   5   10 15 20 25 30 35 40 45 50 55 60 65 70 75 80 85 90 95 100

☐ band members do not play the drum or flute.

Addition and Subtraction Problem Types

	Result Unknown	Change Unknown	Start Unknown
Add To	Aisha has 46 stamps in her collection. Then her grandfather gives her 29 stamps. How many stamps does she have now? *Situation and Solution Equation:* $46 + 29 = \square$	Aisha has 46 stamps in her collection. Then her grandfather gives her some stamps. Now she has 75 stamps. How many stamps did her grandfather give her? *Situation Equation:* $46 + \square = 75$ *Solution Equation:* $\square = 75 - 46$	Aisha has some stamps in her collection. Then her grandfather gives her 29 stamps. Now she has 75 stamps. How many stamps did she have to start? *Situation Equation:* $\square + 29 = 75$ *Solution Equation:* $\square = 75 - 29$
Take From	A store has 43 bottles of water at the start of the day. During the day, the store sells 25 bottles. How many bottles do they have at the end of the day? *Situation and Solution Equation:* $43 - 25 = \square$	A store has 43 bottles of water at the start of the day. The store has 18 bottles left at the end of the day. How many bottles does the store sell? *Situation Equation:* $43 - \square = 18$ *Solution Equation:* $\square = 43 - 18$	A store sells 25 bottles of water during one day. At the end of the day 18 bottles are left. How many bottles did the store have at the beginning of the day? *Situation Equation:* $\square - 25 = 18$ *Solution Equation:* $\square = 25 + 18$

[1]A situation equation represents the structure (action) in the problem situation. A solution equation shows the operation used to find the answer.

Addition and Subtraction Problem Types (continued)

	Total Unknown	Addend Unknown	Other Addend Unknown
Put Together/ Take Apart	A clothing store has 39 shirts with short sleeves and 45 shirts with long sleeves. How many shirts does the store have in all? *Math Drawing²:* *Situation and Solution Equation:* $39 + 45 = \square$	Of the 84 shirts in a clothing store, 39 have short sleeves. The rest have long sleeves. How many shirts have long sleeves? *Math Drawing:* 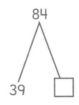 *Situation Equation:* $84 = 39 + \square$ *Solution Equation:* $84 - 39 = \square$	A clothing store has 84 shirts. Some of the shirts have short sleeves, and 45 shirts have long sleeves. How many shirts have short sleeves? *Math Drawing:* 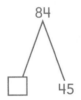 *Situation Equation:* $84 = \square + 45$ *Solution Equation:* $84 - 45 = \square$

Both Addends Unknown is a productive extension of this basic situation, especially for small numbers less than or equal to 10. Such take-apart situations can be used to show all the decompositions of a given number. The associated equations, which have the total on the left of the equal sign, help children understand that the = sign does not always mean *makes* or *results in* but does always mean *is the same number as.*

Both Addends Unknown

Pam has 24 roses. How many can she put in her red vase and how many in her blue vase?

Math Drawing:

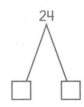

Situation Equation:
$24 = \square + \square$

²These math drawings are called Math Mountains in Grades 1–3 and break-apart drawings in Grades 4 and 5.

Addition and Subtraction Problem Types (continued)

	Difference Unknown	Greater Unknown	Smaller Unknown
Compare[1]	Alex has 64 trading cards. Lucy has 48 trading cards. How many more trading cards does Alex have than Lucy? Lucy has 48 trading cards. Alex has 64 trading cards. How many fewer trading cards does Lucy have than Alex? *Math Drawing:* A ☐ 64 L ☐ 48 ⬭? *Situation Equation:* $48 + \square = 64$ or $\square = 64 - 48$ *Solution Equation:* $\square = 64 - 48$	**Leading Language** Lucy has 48 trading cards. Alex has 16 more trading cards than Lucy. How many trading cards does Alex have? **Misleading Language** Lucy has 48 trading cards. Lucy has 16 fewer trading cards than Alex. How many trading cards does Alex have? *Math Drawing:* A ☐ ? L ☐ 48 ⬭16 *Situation and Solution Equation:* $48 + 16 = \square$	**Leading Language** Alex has 64 trading cards. Lucy has 16 fewer trading cards than Alex. How many trading cards does Lucy have? **Misleading Language** Alex has 64 trading cards. Alex has 16 more trading cards than Lucy. How many trading cards does Lucy have? *Math Drawing:* A ☐ 64 L ☐ ? ⬭16 *Situation Equation:* $\square + 16 = 64$ or $\square = 64 - 16$ *Solution Equation:* $\square = 64 - 16$

[1]A comparison sentence can always be said in two ways. One way uses *more*, and the other uses *fewer* or *less*. Misleading language suggests the wrong operation. For example, it says *Lucy has 16 fewer trading cards than Alex*, but you have to add 16 cards to the number of cards Lucy has to get the number of cards Alex has.

Glossary

5-groups*

||||| ||||| tens in 5-groups

○○○○○
○○○○○   ones in 5-groups

A

add

$$4 + 2 = 6$$

addend

$$5 + 6 = 11$$

↑   ↑

addends

Adding Up Method* (for Subtraction)

$$\begin{array}{r} 144 \\ -\ 68 \\ \hline 76 \end{array}$$

$$68 + 2 = 70$$
$$70 + 30 = 100$$
$$100 + 44 = 144$$
$$\boxed{76}$$

addition doubles*

Both addends (or partners) are the same.
$$4 + 4 = 8$$

A.M.

Use A.M. for times between midnight and noon.

analog clock

angle

These are angles.

array

This rectangular array has 3 rows and 5 columns.

*A classroom research-based term developed for *Math Expressions*

B

bar graph

Coins in My Collection

horizontal
bar graph

Flowers in My Garden

vertical
bar graph

break-apart*

You can break apart a larger number to get two smaller amounts called break-aparts.

10

6   4

break-aparts of 10

C

cent

front   back

1 cent or 1¢ or $0.01

centimeter (cm)

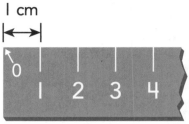

1 cm

0 1 2 3 4

cent sign

56¢

↑

cent sign

circle

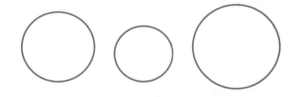

clock

analog clock

digital clock

12:30

*A classroom research-based term developed for *Math Expressions*

columns

This rectangular array has 4 columns with 3 tiles in each column.

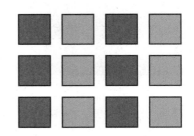

compare numbers

Compare numbers using >, <, or =.

$52 > 25$

$25 < 52$

$25 = 25$

comparison bars*

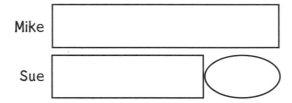

You can add labels and fill in numbers to help you solve *Compare* problems.

cone

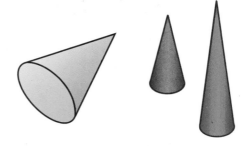

count all*

$5 + 3 = \square$

$5 + 3 = 8$

count on

$5 + 3 = \boxed{8}$

$5 + \boxed{3} = 8$

$8 - 5 = \boxed{3}$

Already **5**

cube

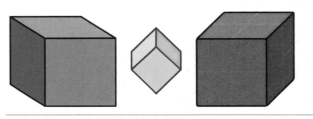

cylinder

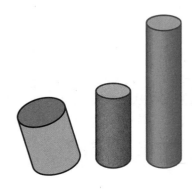

*A classroom research-based term developed for *Math Expressions*

D

data

	Sisters	Brothers
Kendra	2	1
Scott	2	0
Ida	0	1

data

The data in the table show how many sisters and how many brothers each child has.

decade numbers*

10, 20, 30, 40, 50, 60, 70, 80, 90

decimal point

$4.25

decimal point

diagonal

diagonal

difference

$11 - 3 = 8$

$$\begin{array}{r} 11 \\ -\ 3 \\ \hline 8 \end{array}$$

difference → 8

digital clock

12:30

digits

0, 1, 2, 3, 4, 5, 6, 7, 8, 9

15 is a 2-digit number.

The 1 in 15 means 1 ten.

The 5 in 15 means 5 ones.

dime

front   back

10 cents or 10¢ or $0.10

dollar

100 cents or 100¢ or $1.00

 front

 back

dollar sign

$4.25

dollar sign

doubles minus 1

7 + 7 = 14, so

7 + 6 = 13, 1 less than 14.

doubles minus 2

7 + 7 = 14, so

7 + 5 = 12, 2 less than 14.

*A classroom research-based term developed for *Math Expressions*

doubles plus 1

6 + 6 = 12, so

6 + 7 = 13, 1 more than 12.

doubles plus 2

6 + 6 = 12, so

6 + 8 = 14, 2 more than 12.

E

equal shares

2 halves	4 fourths
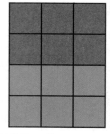	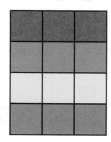

equation

$$4 + 3 = 7 \qquad 7 = 4 + 3$$
$$9 - 5 = 4 \qquad 4 + 5 = 8 + 1$$

An equation must have an = sign.

equation chain*

$$3 + 4 = 5 + 2 = 8 - 1 = 7$$

estimate

Make a reasonable guess about how many or how much.

even

A number is even if you can make groups of 2 and have none left over.

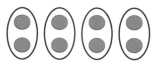

8 is an even number.

exact change

I will pay with 4 dimes and 3 pennies. That is the exact change. I won't get any money back.

expanded form

$$283 = 200 + 80 + 3$$

Expanded Method (for Addition)*

$$
\begin{array}{rcl}
78 & = & 70 + 8 \\
+\,57 & = & 50 + 7 \\
\hline
& & 120 + 15 = 135
\end{array}
$$

Expanded Method* (for Subtraction)

$$
\begin{array}{rcl}
64 & = & \overset{50}{\cancel{60}} + \overset{14}{\cancel{4}} \\
-\,28 & = & 20 + 8 \\
\hline
& & 30 + 6 = 36
\end{array}
$$

*A classroom research-based term developed for *Math Expressions*

extra information

Franny has 8 kittens and 2 dogs. 4 kittens are asleep. How many kittens are awake?

$$8 - 4 = \boxed{4}$$

The number of dogs is extra information. It is not needed to solve the problem.

F

fewer

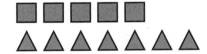

There are fewer ■ than ▲.

foot (ft)

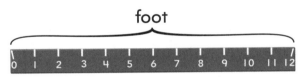

12 inches = 1 foot   (not drawn to scale)

fourths

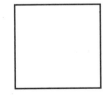

square

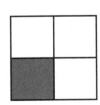

The picture shows 4 fourths. A fourth of the square is shaded.

G

greatest

25   41   63

63 is the greatest number.

group name*

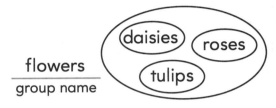

flowers
group name

H

half hour

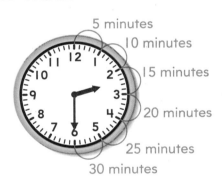

5 minutes
10 minutes
15 minutes
20 minutes
25 minutes
30 minutes

30 minutes = 1 half hour

halves

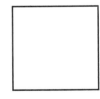

square

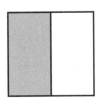

The picture shows 2 halves. A half of the square is shaded.

*A classroom research-based term developed for *Math Expressions*

hexagon

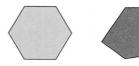

A hexagon has 6 sides and 6 angles.

hidden information

Heather bought a dozen eggs. She used 7 of them to make breakfast. How many eggs does she have left?

$$12 - 7 = \boxed{5}$$

The hidden information is that a dozen means 12.

horizontal bar graph

horizontal form

$$4 + 5 = 9$$

horizontal line

hour

60 minutes = 1 hour

hour hand

hundreds

3 hundreds

347 has 3 hundreds.

↑
hundreds

I

inch (in.)

1 inch

is equal to (=)

$5 + 3 = 8$

5 plus 3 is equal to 8.

is greater than (>)

34 > 25

34 is greater than 25.

is less than (<)

45 < 46

45 is less than 46.

L

least

14   7   63

7 is the least number.

length

The length of the pencil is about 17 cm.
(not drawn to scale)

line plot

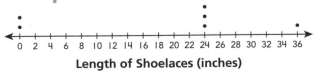

Length of Shoelaces (inches)

line segment

M

make a ten

$8 + 6 = \square$

8 •• | ••••

10 + 4

10 + 4 = 14,

so 8 + 6 = 14

matching drawing*

fewer

more

Math Mountain*

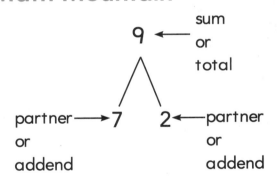

9 ← sum
or
total

partner → 7   2 ← partner
or   or
addend   addend

meter (m)

100 centimeters = 1 meter
(not drawn to scale)

minus

$8 - 3 = 5$

$$\begin{array}{r} 8 \\ -\ 3 \\ \hline 5 \end{array}$$

8 minus 3 equals 5.

*A classroom research-based term developed for *Math Expressions*

minute

60 seconds = 1 minute

minute hand

minute hand: points to the minutes

more

There are more ⬤ than ◼.

New Groups Above Method*

$$\begin{array}{r} \overset{1}{56} \\ + 28 \\ \hline 84 \end{array}$$

6 + 8 = 14
The 1 new ten in 14 goes up above the tens place.

New Groups Below Method*

$$\begin{array}{r} 56 \\ + 28 \\ \hline 84 \end{array}$$

6 + 8 = 14
The 1 new ten in 14 goes below in the tens place.

nickel

front   back

5 cents or 5¢ or $0.05

not equal to (≠)

$$6 + 4 \neq 8$$

6 + 4 is not equal to 8.

number line diagram

0 1 2 3 4 5 6 7 8 9 10

This is a number line diagram.

number name

12

twelve ⟵ number name

odd

A number is odd if you can make groups of 2 and have 1 left over.

9 is an odd number.

*A classroom research-based term developed for *Math Expressions*

ones

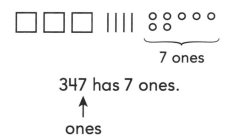

7 ones

347 has 7 ones.

↑ ones

opposite operations

Addition and subtraction are opposite operations.

$$5 + 9 = 14$$
$$14 - 9 = 5$$

Use addition to check subtraction. Use subtraction to check addition.

opposite sides

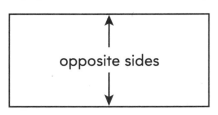

opposite sides

order

2, 5, 6

The numbers 2, 5, and 6 are in order from least to greatest.

P

pairs

A group of 2 is a pair.

The picture shows 4 pairs of counters.

partner lengths*

partner lengths of 4 cm

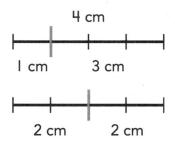

4 cm

1 cm   3 cm

2 cm   2 cm

partners*

$$9 + 6 = 15$$

↑   ↑

partners (addends)

pattern

This pattern shows counting by 2s.

2, 4, 6, 8, 10

penny

front   back

1 cent or 1¢ or $0.01

pentagon

A pentagon has 5 sides and 5 angles.

*A classroom research-based term developed for *Math Expressions*

picture graph

Apples	🍎🍎🍎🍎🍎🍎🍎
Oranges	🟠🟠🟠🟠🟠🟠🟠🟠🟠

plus

$3 + 2 = 5$

3 plus 2 equals 5.

$$\begin{array}{r} 3 \\ +\ 2 \\ \hline 5 \end{array}$$

P.M.

Use P.M. for times between noon and midnight.

proof drawing*

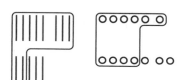

$86 + 57 = 143$

Q

quadrilateral

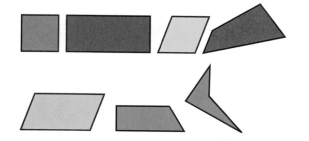

A quadrilateral has 4 sides and 4 angles.

quarter

front   back

25 cents or 25¢ or $0.25

A quarter is another name for a fourth.

A quarter is a fourth of a dollar.

quarter-hour

15 minutes = 1 quarter-hour

quick hundreds*

quick hundreds

quick tens*

quick tens

*A classroom research-based term developed for *Math Expressions*

rectangle

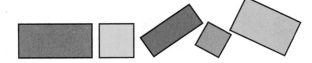

A rectangle has 4 sides and 4 right angles. Opposite sides have the same length.

rectangular prism

right angle

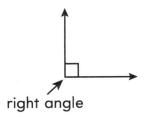

right angle

A right angle is sometimes called a *square corner*.

round

Express a number to the nearest ten or hundred. You can round down or round up.

52 ⟶ 50   278 ⟶ 300

rows

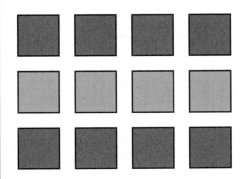

This rectangular array has 3 rows with 4 tiles in each row.

ruler

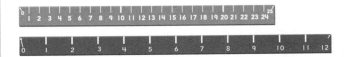

A ruler is used to measure length.

S

scale

The numbers along the side or the bottom of a graph are the scale.

Show All Totals Method*

```
   25            724
 + 48          + 158
   60            800
   13             70
   73             12
                 882
```

situation equation*

A baker baked 100 loaves of bread. He sold some loaves. There are 73 loaves left. How many loaves of bread did he sell?

$$100 - \boxed{} = 73$$

situation equation

skip count

skip count by 2s: 2, 4, 6, 8, . . .
skip count by 5s: 5, 10, 15, 20, . . .
skip count by 10s: 10, 20, 30, 40, 50, . . .

solution equation*

A baker baked 100 loaves of bread. He sold some loaves. There are 73 loaves left. How many loaves of bread did he sell?

$$100 - 73 = \boxed{}$$

solution equation

sphere

square

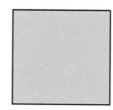

A square has 4 equal sides and 4 right angles.

subtract

$$8 - 5 = 3$$

subtraction doubles*

The subtrahend and the difference, or partners, are the same.
$$8 - 4 = 4$$

sum

$$4 + 3 = 7$$

```
        4
      + 3
sum ──▶ 7
```

survey

When you collect data by asking people questions, you are taking a survey.

*A classroom research-based term developed for *Math Expressions*

T

tally chart

Our Favorite Pets

Pet	Tally	Number
Fish	IIII	4
Dogs	IIII IIII	10
Cats	IIII II	7

teen number

any number from 11 to 19

11 12 13 14 15 16 17 18 19

tens

4 tens

347 has 4 tens.

tens

thirds

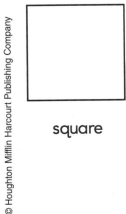

square

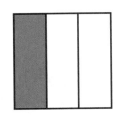

The picture shows 3 thirds. A third of the square is shaded.

thousand

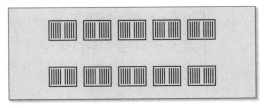

1,000 = 10 hundreds

total

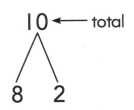

10 ← total

8   2

trapezoid

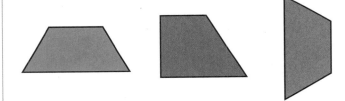

triangle

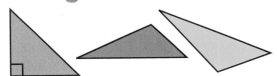

A triangle has 3 sides and 3 angles.

U

ungroup*

Ungroup when you need more ones or tens to subtract.

*A classroom research-based term developed for *Math Expressions*

Ungroup First Method*

```
  6 4
- 2 8
  ↑ ↑
 yes no
```

```
  5|4
  ⁶/4
- 2 8
```

```
  5|4
  ⁶/4
- 2 8
─────
  3 6
```

1. Check to see if there are enough tens and ones to subtract.

2. You can get more ones by taking from the tens and putting them in the ones place.

3. Subtract from either right to left or left to right.

unknown addend

$$3 + \boxed{} = 9$$

↑
unknown addend

unknown total

$$3 + 6 = \boxed{}$$

↑
unknown total

V

vertical bar graph

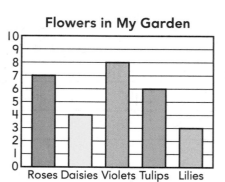

Flowers in My Garden

vertical form

$$\begin{array}{r} 4 \\ + 3 \\ \hline 7 \end{array}$$

vertical line

view

This is the side view of the rectangular prism above.

*A classroom research-based term developed for *Math Expressions*

W

width

width or length

length width

Y

yard (yd)

3 feet = 1 yard

(not drawn to scale)

2.ARO Algebraic Reasoning and Operations

2.ARO.1	Create and solve one- and two-step real-world addition and subtraction word problems through 100 involving *adding to, putting together, taking from, taking apart,* and *comparing,* that have unknown quantities in all positions; represent problems using pictures, equations that have a symbol, including letters, for the unknown quantity, or other methods.	Unit 1 Lessons 1, 2, 4, 5, 9, 10, 11, 12, 13, 14, 15, 16, 17, 18, 19, 20, 21; Unit 2 Lessons 1, 2, 6, 7, 8, 15; Unit 4 Lessons 3, 4, 5, 12, 13, 14, 16, 17, 18, 19, 20, 21, 22, 23; Unit 5 Lessons 3, 4, 5, 6, 7, 8, 9, 10; Unit 6 Lesson 15; Unit 7 Lessons 3, 4, 5
2.ARO.2	Demonstrate fluency in adding and subtracting through 20 using mental math strategies. Know the sums of two one-digit numbers from memory by the end of Grade 2.	Unit 1 Lessons 1, 2, 3, 4, 5, 7, 8, 9, 10, 11, 12, 13, 14, 15, 16, 17, 18, 19, 20, 21; Unit 2 Lessons 2, 6; Unit 3 Lessons 1, 3, 4; Unit 4 Lessons 6, 13; Unit 5 Lessons 3, 4, 5, 6, 7, 9, 10; Unit 7 Lesson 6
2.ARO.3	Use pairing or counting by twos to decide if a group of objects through 20 represents an odd or even number of items. Write an equation to show that an even number can be expressed as the sum of two equal addends.	Unit 1 Lessons 6, 7, 21; Unit 7 Lesson 1
2.ARO.4	Add to find the number of objects in rectangular arrays that have as many as five rows and five columns; use an equation to represent the total as the sum of equal addends.	Unit 7 Lessons 1, 6
2.ARO.5	Identify, create and describe simple number patterns involving repeated addition or subtraction, skip counting and arrays of objects such as counters or tiles. Use patterns to solve problems in various contexts.	Unit 1 Lessons, 6, 21; Unit 2 Lesson 15; Unit 3 Lesson 9; Unit 4 Lessons 1, 23; Unit 5 Lesson 10; Unit 6 Lesson 15; Unit 7 Lessons 1, 6

2.PVO Place Value and Operations

2.PVO.1	Given a three-digit number, understand that the three digits represent hundreds, tens, and ones—for example, 358 = 3 hundreds 5 tens 8 ones.	Unit 2 Lessons 1, 2, 3, 4, 5, 6, 7, 8, 9, 10, 11; Unit 4 Lessons 7, 8, 9, 10, 12; Unit 6 Lessons 1, 2, 3, 4, 10, 11, 12
2.PVO.1.a	Understand that 100 can be thought of as a group of 10 tens named *one hundred*.	Unit 2 Lessons 1, 2, 3, 4, 6, 7, 8, 9, 11; Unit 4 Lessons 3, 4, 7, 8, 9, 10, 12; Unit 6 Lessons 1, 4, 6, 7, 9, 10, 11, 13
2.PVO.1.b	Understand that the numbers 100 through 900 represent 1 hundred through 9 hundreds and 0 tens 0 ones.	Unit 4 Lesson 7; Unit 6 Lesson 1
2.PVO.2	Count through 1000 starting at any number and skip-count through 1000 by 5s, 10s, and 100s.	Unit 1 Lesson 6; Unit 2 Lessons 1, 2, 3, 12, 15; Unit 4 Lessons 1, 2, 15; Unit 5 Lesson 2; Unit 6 Lessons 1, 4
2.PVO.3	Use base-ten numerals, names for numbers, and expanded form to read and write numbers to 1000 (example: 973, nine hundred seventy-three, 900 + 70 + 3).	Unit 2 Lessons 1, 2, 3, 4, 5; Unit 6 Lessons 1, 2, 4
2.PVO.4	Compare and order numbers through 1000 using understanding of place value; record the results with the symbol >, <, or =.	Unit 2 Lessons 5, 15; Unit 5 Lesson 10; Unit 6 Lessons 3, 15

Mathematical Standards

2.PVO Place Value and Operations

2.PVO.5	Demonstrate fluency in adding and subtracting through 100 applying properties of operations, place value, and the relationship between addition and subtraction.	Unit 2 Lessons 2, 4, 13, 14, 15; Unit 3 Lesson 9; Unit 4 Lessons 1, 2, 3, 4, 5, 6, 11, 12, 13, 14, 15, 16, 17, 18, 19, 20, 21, 22, 23; Unit 5 Lessons 5, 8, 9; Unit 6 Lessons 3, 8, 10, 15; Unit 7 Lessons 3, 4, 5
2.PVO.6	Use strategies involving properties of operations and place value to add two through four 2-digit numbers.	Unit 2 Lessons 6, 7, 8, 9, 10, 11, 14, 15; Unit 4 Lessons 3, 5, 12, 15, 16, 17, 18; Unit 7 Lessons 4, 5
2.PVO.7	Use objects or pictures and strategies involving place value, properties of operations, or the relationship between addition and subtraction to add and subtract through 1000; show how the chosen strategy and the recorded result are connected. Understand that to add or subtract 3-digit numbers, add/subtract *hundreds and hundreds, tens and tens, ones and ones;* recognize that in some instances it is necessary to group or ungroup tens or hundreds.	Unit 2 Lessons 4, 6, 7, 8, 9, 10, 11, 14, 15; Unit 3 Lesson 6; Unit 4 Lessons 3, 4, 5, 6, 7, 8, 9, 10, 12, 13, 15, 16, 17, 18, 19, 20; Unit 5 Lesson 9; Unit 6 Lessons 2, 4, 5, 6, 7, 8, 9, 10, 11, 12, 13, 14, 15
2.PVO.8	Use mental math: to add 10 or 100 to a number 100 through 900, and to subtract 10 or 100 from a number 100 through 900. Round numbers up to the nearest 10 and 100 and round numbers down to the nearest 10 and 100. Estimate sums and differences up to 100.	Unit 2 Lesson 4; Unit 4 Lesson 14; Unit 6 Lessons 2, 4, 12
2.PVO.9	Use place value and the properties of operations to explain why strategies for addition and subtraction work.	Unit 1 Lessons 1, 3, 4, 5, 7, 10, 11, 16, 20; Unit 2 Lessons 2, 4, 6, 7, 8, 9, 10; Unit 4 Lessons 3, 4, 5, 6, 7, 8, 9, 10, 11, 12, 14, 15, 16, 17, 18; Unit 6 Lessons 2, 5, 6, 7, 8, 9, 10, 11, 12, 13, 14, 15; Unit 7 Lessons 4, 5

2.MDA Measurement and Data Analysis

2.MDA.1	Select and use the appropriate tool to measure the length of a given object (examples of tools: ruler, yardstick, tape measure, meter stick).	Unit 3 Lessons 1, 2, 3, 4, 6, 7, 8, 9; Unit 4 Lesson 23; Unit 7 Lesson 1
2.MDA.2	Use two different standard units of length –for example, inches and centimeters –to measure an object twice, and explain how the size of the chosen units affects the resulting measurements (example: larger units result in fewer units used, smaller units result in more units used).	Unit 3 Lessons 7, 8, 9
2.MDA.3	Estimate the lengths of objects in inches, feet, centimeters, and meters.	Unit 3 Lessons 3, 4, 6; Unit 4 Lesson 23
2.MDA.4	Find how much longer one object is than another using standard units to measure; record the difference in length labeling the result with the unit that was used.	Unit 3 Lessons 1, 2, 6; Unit 4 Lesson 23
2.MDA.5	Solve addition and subtraction word problems involving lengths measured in the same units and containing numbers through 100; represent the problems using pictures for example, drawing rulers, writing equations that include a symbol for the unknown quantity, or other methods that work.	Unit 4 Lesson 23; Unit 7 Lessons 3, 4, 5
2.MDA.6	Understand and show that whole numbers can be represented as lengths on a number line, and that the number line is made up of equally-spaced points starting at 0 and continuing 1, 2, 3, …; represent sums and differences through 100 on the number line.	Unit 7 Lessons 3, 5
2.MDA.7	Identify and write the time using analog and digital clocks to the quarter-hour and to the nearest five minutes, using A.M. and P.M. Know the relationships of time.	Unit 5 Lessons 1, 2
2.MDA.8	Solve word problems that involve pennies, nickels, dimes, quarters, and dollars; correctly use the symbols ¢ and $.	Unit 2 Lessons 11, 12, 15; Unit 4 Lessons 1,2, 10, 15; Unit 5 Lessons 3, 5

2.MDA Measurement and Data Analysis

2.MDA.9	Create data by measuring the lengths of several objects in whole units, or by having different individuals measure the same object. Make a line plot with a whole-number scale to display the data.	Unit 3 Lessons 6, 7, 8
2.MDA.10	Display data containing a maximum of 4 categories in a table, picture graph, and a bar graph (that has a scale of just single units). Solve problems involving *putting-together, taking-apart,* and *comparing* contexts using data from a bar graph.	Unit 5 Lessons 3, 4, 5, 6, 7, 8, 9, 10

2.GSR Geometry and Spatial Reasoning

2.GSR.1	Given specific attributes of a geometric figure for example number of equal sides, name and draw the figure. Identify two-dimensional figures—*triangles, quadrilaterals, pentagons, hexagons*—and the three-dimensional figure, *cube.* Classify two-dimensional figures as polygons or non-polygons.	Unit 3 Lessons 2, 3, 4, 5, 9; Unit 7 Lessons 1, 2, 4, 5
2.GSR.1.a	Identify and name basic two- and three-dimensional shapes, such as squares, circles, triangles, rectangles, trapezoids, hexagons, cubes, rectangular prisms, cones, cylinders and spheres.	Unit 3 Lessons 2, 5; Unit 7 Lessons 1, 2, 4, 5
2.GSR.1.b	Describe, compare, and classify two- and three-dimensional figures according to number and shape of faces, and the number of sides, edges and vertices (corners).	Unit 3 Lessons 2, 5; Unit 7 Lesson 5
2.GSR.2	Separate a rectangle into equal-size squares by creating rows and columns; use counting to find the total number of squares.	Unit 7 Lessons 1, 6
2.GSR.3	Separate rectangles and circles into 2, 3, and 4 equal shares; identify the equal-size shares as *halves, thirds, fourths, half of, a third of,* and *a fourth of;* use the terms *two halves, three thirds,* and *four fourths* to describe the whole. Understand that wholes with the same shape/size can have equal shares that are different shapes.	Unit 5 Lesson 2; Unit 7 Lessons 1, 2, 6

MPP1

Problem Solving

Unit 1 Lessons 2, 3, 4, 5, 6, 7, 9, 10, 11, 12, 13, 14, 15, 16, 17, 18, 19, 20, 21
Unit 2 Lessons 1, 4, 5, 6, 7, 8, 9, 11, 12, 13, 14, 15
Unit 3 Lessons 1, 3, 5, 6, 7, 9
Unit 4 Lessons 1, 2, 3, 4, 5, 6, 7, 8, 9, 10, 11, 12, 13, 14, 16, 17, 18, 19, 20, 21, 22, 23
Unit 5 Lessons 1, 2, 3, 4, 5, 6, 7, 8, 9, 10
Unit 6 Lessons 1, 4, 5, 6, 8, 9, 10, 12, 14, 15
Unit 7 Lessons 1, 2, 3, 4, 5, 6

MPP2

Abstract and Quantitative Reasoning

Unit 1 Lessons 1, 5, 7, 8, 9, 10, 11, 14, 20, 21
Unit 2 Lessons 1, 3, 4, 5, 6, 7, 8, 9, 11, 12, 13, 14, 15
Unit 3 Lessons 1, 2, 3, 5, 7, 8, 9
Unit 4 Lessons 1, 2, 3, 4, 5, 6, 7, 8, 9, 10, 11, 12, 13, 15, 17, 19, 20, 22, 23
Unit 5 Lessons 1, 2, 3, 5,10
Unit 6 Lessons 1, 2, 3, 4, 10, 12, 15
Unit 7 Lessons 1, 2, 3, 4, 5, 6

MPP3

Use and Evaluate Logical Reasoning

Unit 1 Lessons 1, 2, 3, 4, 5, 6, 7, 8, 9, 10, 11, 12, 13, 14, 15, 16, 17, 18, 19, 20, 21
Unit 2 Lessons 1, 2, 3, 4, 5, 6, 7, 8, 9, 10, 12, 13, 14, 15
Unit 3 Lessons 1, 2, 3, 4, 5, 6, 7, 8, 9
Unit 4 Lessons 1, 2, 3, 4, 5, 6, 7, 8, 9, 10, 11, 12, 13, 14, 15, 16, 17, 18, 19, 20, 21, 22, 23
Unit 5 Lessons 1, 2, 3, 4, 5, 6, 7, 8, 9, 10
Unit 6 Lessons 1, 2, 3, 4, 5, 6, 7, 8, 9, 10, 11, 12, 13, 14, 15
Unit 7 Lessons 1, 2, 3, 4, 5, 6

MPP4

Mathematical Modeling

Unit 1 Lessons 5, 10, 11, 12, 13, 14, 15, 16, 17, 18, 19, 20, 21
Unit 2 Lessons 1, 2, 3, 4, 5, 6, 7, 8, 11, 12, 13, 14, 15
Unit 3 Lessons 1, 2, 3, 6, 7, 8, 9
Unit 4 Lessons 1, 3, 4, 5, 7, 10, 12, 13, 14, 18, 19, 20, 21, 23
Unit 5 Lessons 3, 5, 7, 8, 9, 10
Unit 6 Lessons 1, 5, 9, 11, 12, 14, 15
Unit 7 Lessons 1, 3, 6

Mathematical Processes and Practices

MPP5

Use Mathematical Tools

Unit 1 Lessons 3, 6, 20, 21
Unit 2 Lessons 1, 2, 3, 4, 5, 8, 12, 13, 14, 15
Unit 3 Lessons 1, 2, 3, 5, 6, 7, 8, 9
Unit 4 Lessons 1, 2, 3, 4, 7, 8, 9, 11, 18, 23
Unit 5 Lessons 1, 2, 5, 10
Unit 6 Lessons 1, 2, 5, 7, 10, 15
Unit 7 Lessons 1, 2, 3, 6

MPP6

Use Precise Mathematical Language

Unit 1 Lessons 1, 2, 3, 4, 5, 6, 7, 8, 9, 10, 11, 12, 13, 14, 15, 16, 17, 18, 19, 20, 21
Unit 2 Lessons 1, 2, 3, 4, 5, 6, 7, 8, 9, 10, 11, 12, 13, 14, 15
Unit 3 Lessons 1, 2, 3, 4, 5, 6, 7, 8, 9
Unit 4 Lessons 1, 2, 3, 4, 5, 6, 7, 8, 9, 10, 12, 13, 14, 15, 16, 17, 18, 19, 20, 21, 22, 23
Unit 5 Lessons 1, 2, 3, 4, 5, 6, 7, 8, 9, 10
Unit 6 Lessons 1, 2, 3, 4, 5, 6, 7, 8, 9, 10, 11, 12, 13, 14, 15
Unit 7 Lessons 1, 2, 3, 4, 5, 6

MPP7

See Structure

Unit 1 Lessons 1, 2, 3, 5, 6, 9, 13, 17, 18, 19, 20, 21
Unit 2 Lessons 1, 2, 3, 4, 6, 10, 11, 12, 15
Unit 3 Lessons 1, 3, 4, 5, 6, 7, 8, 9
Unit 4 Lessons 1, 2, 7, 13, 17, 19, 21, 23
Unit 5 Lessons 2, 6, 7, 10
Unit 6 Lessons 4, 12, 13, 15
Unit 7 Lessons 1, 2, 6

MPP8

Generalize

Unit 1 Lessons 2, 6, 7, 21
Unit 2 Lessons 3, 5, 10, 11, 15
Unit 3 Lessons 1, 2, 7, 8, 9
Unit 4 Lessons 4, 8, 13, 23
Unit 5 Lessons 2, 10
Unit 6 Lessons 2, 4, 7, 8, 12, 15
Unit 7 Lessons 2, 6

© Houghton Mifflin Harcourt Publishing Company

Index

Even, 27–28

Expanded form, 97, 98, 332

Expanded Method, 214, 217, 221

F

Family Letter, 1–2, 7–8, 39–40, 89–90, 107–108, 145–146, 167–168, 197–198, 215–216, 271–272, 289–290, 323–324, 341–342, 353–354, 383–384

Fewer, 49–50

Fluency
  addition within 20, 36, 50, 110, 220
  addition within 100, 129–132, 239–240, 248, 256, 300, 308, 334, 350, 358
  Check, 38, 60, 82, 106, 120, 138, 166, 190, 210, 234, 264, 288, 296, 316, 340, 352, 366, 398, 414
  subtraction within 20, 36, 50, 110, 220
  subtraction within 100, 229–230, 239–240, 248, 256, 300, 308, 334, 350, 358

Foot (ft), 181

Fourths, 391–392
  of a rectangle, 395

Fractions
  equal shares, 391–392, 393, 396
  fourths, 391–392
  halves, 391–392
  thirds, 391–392

G

Games
  New Ten Challenge, 131–132
  Ungroup Challenge, 231–232

Geometry
  angles, 151–154
  attributes, 162–164
    corners, 151–154
    faces, 163–164
    sides of, 151–154
  different shape but same size, 396
  distance around shapes, 156–158, 405–406
  identifying shapes, 162
  three-dimensional solids
    combine/compose, 163
    classify, 164
    cone, 162–164
    cube, 162–164
    cylinder, 162–164
    rectangular prisms, 159, 162–164
    relating to two-dimensional shapes, 164
    sort, 164
    sphere, 162–164
  two-dimensional shapes
    circle, 162–164
    hexagon, 154, 162–164, 187–188
    pentagon, 154, 162–164, 187–188
    quadrilateral, 154, 162–164, 187–188
    rectangle, 152, 156, 162–164
    square, 151, 155, 162–164, 396
    trapezoid, 162–164
    triangle, 153, 157–158, 162–164, 187–188

Graphs
  bar graph, 298–299, 301–302, 303–304, 309, 310–311
    horizontal, 301–302, 303, 305
    vertical, 301–302, 304, 306
  organizing data on, 306, 313
  picture graph, 299, 309
    horizontal, 291
    vertical, 292

tally chart, 297–298
using data from a table, 309

Greater than (>), 101–102, 333–334

H

Halves, 391–392
of a rectangle, 395

Height, 172–173
in centimeters and inches, 182

Hexagon, 154, 162–164, 187–188

I

Inch (in), 177–178
compared to centimeters, 182–184, 186

Is equal to (=), 101–102

Is greater than (>), 101–102, 333–334

Is less than (<), 101–102, 333–334

L

Least, 103–104, 333–334

Length, 147–149, 172, 183, 261
addition of, 150
word problems, 407–409

Less than (<), 101–102, 333–334

Line plot, 173–174
for height measurement, 182
for measurement data, 185

M

Make-a-Ten strategy, 17–18, 20

Manipulatives
10-sticks, 97

clock, 275
coin cards, 199, 201
dollar bills with penny array, 325–326
dollars and cents cutouts, 121–122
Circles and Rectangles, 393
Juice Bar, 243
Make-a-Ten cards, 55–58, 75–78
Math Mountain cards, 9, 11
measuring tools
centimeter ruler, 171
inch ruler, 175
meter tape, 169
yardstick, 179
rectangular prisms, 159
Secret Code Cards, 93–94, 131–132, 231–232, 329–330, 338
square-inch tiles, 385

Math Mountains, 32, 368
for addition, 3, 13–14
in compare problems, 53–54
drawing, 6
and equation pairs, 21
equations for, 5–6, 237
make a ten with, 18
modeling word problems with, 68–72
for subtraction, 3, 13–14
for word problem solutions, 235–236

Measurement. *See also* Time.
comparing units of, 186
of distance
around a rectangle, 156
around a square, 155
around a triangle, 157–158
estimation of, 171
in feet and yards, 181
of height, 172–173, 182
of length, 147–149, 171, 183, 261
to the nearest inch, 177–178
of stride, 262

Index

© Houghton Mifflin Harcourt Publishing Company

Index

finding information in a story, 63
with groups of ten, 99
hidden information, 64
length, 399–401, 407–409
mixed, 253–255, 369
with new tens and hundreds, 109–110
not enough information, 61, 64
start unknown, 249–250
subtraction, 13–14, 41–47, 68–71, 73–74, 235–236, 355, 369–372
  within 20, 92, 96, 238
  within 100, 240
three and four lengths, 403
two-step, 67–72, 112, 259-260

ungrouping 100, 211
using letters to represent unknown numbers, 23
using New Groups Below Method, 113–114
using Show All Totals Method, 111
writing, 73–74, 80, 213

Y

Yard (yd), 181

Z

Zeros, subtraction with, 225–226

Illustrator: Josh Brill

Did you ever try to use shapes to draw animals like the platypus on the cover?

Over the last 10 years Josh has been using geometric shapes to design his animals. His aim is to keep the animal drawings simple and use color to make them appealing.

Add some color to the platypus Josh drew. Then try drawing a cat or dog or some other animal using the shapes below.

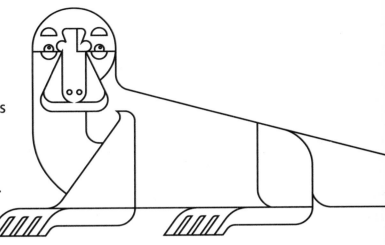

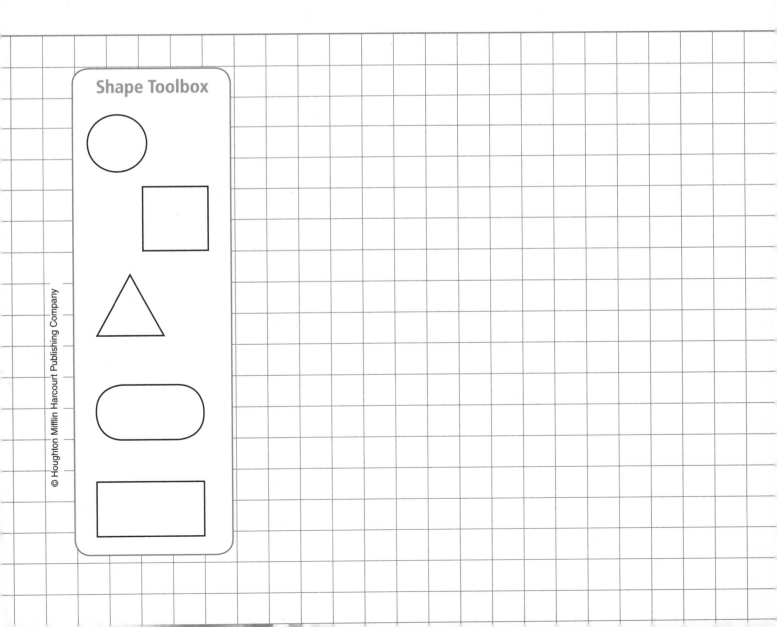

Shape Toolbox